S. J. PERELMAN

Strictly from Hunger

RANDOM HOUSE · NEW YORK

MANUFACTURED IN THE UNITED STATES OF AMERICA

·E H·

To
ADAM

Thanks are due *The New Yorker*, *College Humor*, *Life*, *Judge*, and *Contact* for permission to reprint the material which has appeared in their pages

Contents

INTRODUCTION BY ROBERT BENCHLEY 11

THE RED TERMITES 19

SCENARIO 31

GOOD NEWS, BIBLIOPHILES! 43

THE IDOL'S EYE 49

TAXIDERMY: ITS CAUSE AND CURE 59

STRICTLY FROM HUNGER 65

POISONOUS MUSHROOMS, OR ARE WE AT
    THE CROSSROADS? 83

A FAREWELL TO OMSK 91

ENTERED AS SECOND-CLASS MATTER 99

ANNUAL NAVIGATION REPORT 113

THE LOVE DECOY 119

AVOCADO, OR THE FUTURE OF EATING 129

FOOTNOTE ON THE YELLOW PERIL 137

TEN CENTS IN STAMPS 143

BUFFALOS OF THE WORLD, UNITE! 157

THE KISS FOOL 165

CONTENTS

THE INFANT INDUSTRY   175

THE CASE OF COLONEL BRADSHAW   183

WAITING FOR SANTY   191

DINNER PARTY   199

SEEDLINGS OF DESIRE   211

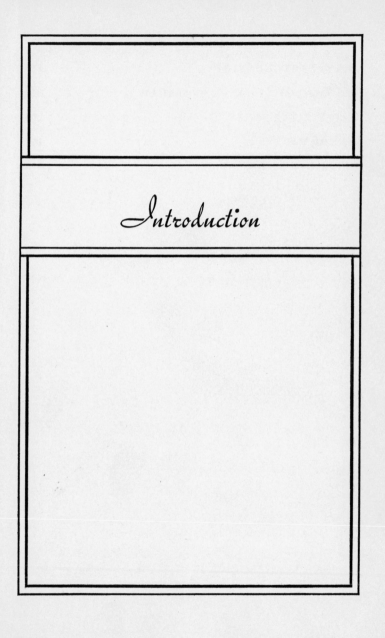

Introduction

$\mathcal{S}$OMEONE once said that writing an introduction to a book is like a pretty girl, but he escaped me before I could find out what he meant by it. I chased and chased him, but he was younger and quicker than I was, and so I never did learn the pay-off.

From here the Nile flows in a northwesterly direction until it reaches the clam-flats, where it is intercepted by countless red and green posters reading "État," meaning that the French government operates the railroads. (This experiment, incidentally, has been highly successful, as witness the white lace antimacassars on the backs of the seats of the railway carriages with the same word "État" embroidered on them.) Here the lagoons become flowering fields and, as the sun sets over the seed-grass, or oil-ducts, we see an entirely different Nile, the Nile of Al-Kahar, of Chinese Gordon, of Brickley, Mahan

and Casey. Also, if one were so minded, the hippopot-
amus gives way to the smaller, but no less ruthless, dick-
dick, and the tropical rains begin.

We can, I feel certain, base our assumption that Swift
was married to Stella (for an assumption it must be
until we have proven our point) on a letter recently
discovered by Heegy in the library of the Orthopedic
Church at Malmsley. Swift (the Gloomy Dean) was
acquainted with Stella. This we know. His preoccupa-
tion with vapors of one sort or another has been shown
in *A Discourse Concerning the Automatic Operation of
the Spirit, Inspired on the Occasion of the Seventh
Birthday of Sir William Temple* ('89). LeBaudy's testimony confirms the other biographers, Raglan's in particular, and we are safe to assume that when he wrote: "I
had te [the?] 100 bs. in my Pocket" he meant that he
had already brought some sort of culmination to his rela-
tions with Stella, or Vanessa, as she was later to be
known.

Somehow, I like Mrs. Ramm's translation of "*Io son,
cantava, io son dolce sirena*" better. Mrs. Ramm gives
it this: "She sang: 'I am the siren of sweet sound'."

This, as I see it, has more of the mysterious vision
which visited Dante, more of the Homeric completeness.
You can just hear "dem darkies strummin'," and, for
pictorial effect, there is nothing more lovely than "I kiss

your little hand, Madame" for "*Ce n'est que votre main, Madame.*" Or did I lose my place?

But *how* shall we learn from experience? Call it empiricism, if you will, but empiricism what? James's answer is that we learn actively and not passively. Okeh. But is that all? James found in Hume an "intolerable disintegration of experience." That was all very well for James to say, but he later wrote to Holmes of his "image of ideals being the vanishing points which give a kind of perspective to the chaos of events." What kind of talk is this? There *must* be one thing or another, "else what's a heathen for?"

In conclusion, let me quote from the final plea to the jury of George D. Robinson, Esq., for the Defense:

"So far as you are concerned, this is the last word of the defendant to you. Take it: take care of her as you have, and give us promptly your verdict of 'not guilty', that she may go home and be Lizzie Borden of Fall River in that bloodstained and wrecked home where she has passed her life for so many years."

If the reader (who shall be nameless) has detected a certain lack of cohesion in the preceding introduction to Mr. Perelman's book, it has been due to an equally certain desire on my part to confound Mr. Perelman as he has confounded me. For Mr. Perelman, and I say it with rancor, nipped my writing career in the bud and drove me into movie-acting.

Together with several others of my ilk, most of whom are now on movie relief, thanks to Mr. Perelman, I was making a decent living writing fugitive pieces for the magazines, pieces which, while not pretentious, we fondly imagined sprang from a congenital insanity which could be turned into thirty dollars here or forty dollars there. It was a perfectly good racket, at any rate, and several psychiatrists were good enough to refer to it as "free association," or Dope's Disease.

Then, from the Baptist precincts of Brown University, wafted a cloud no bigger than a man's hams, which was S. J. Perelman. It consisted at first of little drawings with abominably hand-lettered legends, but it held a menace for all of us who were pretending to be insane for profit. Here was the real Magoo, a natural son of the Prophet Da-Da, and he was only an undergraduate.

From then on, it was just a matter of time before Perelman took over the dementia praecox field and drove us all to writing articles on economics for The Commentator. Any further attempts to garble thought-processes sounded like imitation-Perelman. He did to our weak little efforts at "crazy stuff" what Benny Goodman has done to middle-period jazz. He swung it. To use a swing phrase, he took it "out of the world." And there he remains, all by himself.

In the comprehensive index to Max Eastman's somewhat less than comprehensive analysis of Laughter, we find the following section in the list of names under "P".

PEGLER, WESTBROOK.

PENNER, JOE.

PERKINS, ELI.

PERL, R. E.

PHELPS, WILLIAM LYON.

The omission of "Perelman, S. J." from this particular book is not surprising, as he probably didn't bother to answer Mr. Eastman's preliminary questionnaire on "What Is Humor?" But if Ring Lardner had got out a book on American Humor (which he most certainly would never have dreamed of doing), I'll bet that "Perelman, S. J." would have led all the rest in that particular field which Lardner himself loved the best.

ROBERT BENCHLEY

The Red Termites

A STORY FOR

YOUNG STRIKEBREAKERS

CENTREVILLE! All out!"

The conductor's voice rang out in the Pullman, and Avid Lissner, her piquant figure smartly attired in the latest Fifth Avenue creation, added a touch of flour to her nose and arose. Old George, the "darky" porter, beamed paternally at her as he scratched his woolly poll.

"Shall I brush yo'all off, Miss Avid?"

"No, George, I shall descend in the usual way," replied Avid merrily. Her jest was not lost on old George, who chuckled appreciatively and flung her baggage out of the window. Avid descended and found old George, the foreman of her father's factory, awaiting her on the platform. He wiped his grease-covered hands apologetically on her underskirt and shook hands.

"Faix, macushla, hit's sho' glad Ah'm bein' at seein' yez back from college," he said respectfully. "Dem cussed

[21]

Reds has almost got de upper hand, dat dey has! Evah sence yo' poor pappy passed on . . ." He shook his head pessimistically, and several moths fluttered out of it. Avid's lips set grimly and little fires sparkled in her eyes; it was easy to see that her iris was up.

"I'll show those sneaking Nihilists!" she declared angrily. "Coming in here and corrupting our good American workmen with their utopian ideas! If they don't like our country, why don't they go back where they came from? Just imagine, George, they want me to divide everything fifty-fifty with some smelly peasant! That's the trouble with those foreigners, they make all their money over here and then take it back with them to Poland. Hanging's too good for those Socialists!" Unfortunately, Avid's heated words were not lost on a Red spy lurking in the crowd. Bomb in hand, he slunk off sneering evilly and promising revenge.

It was a troubled butler who met Avid at the gates of the Lissner mansion. Old George had raised Avid from a baby he had once had and she had come to love him like a brothel.

"Why, what's the matter, George?" inquired Avid, as she drew off her tight slippers and placed her feet with a sigh in the steaming cauldron of soup bubbling on the fire.

"It's those Reds, miss," confided George in an anxious

whisper. "They've been leaving notes ordering us to eat only black bread and caviar. Only yesterday they held a meeting changing the name of the town to Centregrad. It's all the doings of that Jake (Soviet) Gold." Avid recognized the name as that of a hulking Bolshevist bully who had been swaying the workers with his insidious doctrines. Late into the night she sat thoughtfully in the library, listening to the ballet music from Six Who Pass While the Lentils Boil, and when the first faint flush of dawn and the milkman came peeping into the windows, her plan was ready.

Three hours later, disguised as a workman, a red handkerchief knotted loosely about her forehead and her features thickly daubed with oil, Avid took her place in the swarm of laughing, joyous laborers entering her factory. Soon she was operating a punch-press in a corner of the foundry, keeping her eyes and ears open, you may be sure. Suddenly a hoarse, throaty laugh attracted her attention. Looking up she discerned the lineaments of Jake (Soviet) Gold leering at her.

"Give us a little kiss, comrade," he invited bestially, chucking her under the chin. "A little class-consciousness there, my cabbage!" Avid attempted to repulse him, but he was already crushing her to him. Her shrieks were drowned in the whir of the machinery as his grimy face sought hers. An unexpected blow sent him plunging

[23]

back. Linwood Flowers, a sturdy young American machinist, was confronting him with doubled fists.

"Tell *that* to your Moscow masters," grunted Flowers, as he drove a telling blow into Gold's solar plexus. "I'll teach you to lay your hands on defenseless American girls!"

But the cowardly Communist was already begging for mercy, albeit he could not resist a final threat to Avid.

"Just wait, your time'll come!" he sneered. "You'll be nationalized the same as everybody else! No marriage, do you hear? If two people love each other, all they have to do is sign a certificate!"

"Oh, so that's it—free love, hey?" demanded Flowers, springing at him. But the skulking bully had fled like the craven he was.

"Oh, Linwood!" breathed Avid, as she felt his muscular arms tighten about her. "It all seems so hopeless! Is this alien within our gates to warp the idealism for which our grandfathers fought at Bunker Hill, Chicken Ridge and Mungerstown? Was it for this that Montcalm faced Wolfe on the snowy heights of Quebec? And, just think, they won't even let you take a bath under Communism! Oh, Linwood . . ."

"There, there, Avid," he soothed her. "We'll win through yet, and when we do . . ." His eyes held an unspoken question. She nodded, a blush tinging her

[24]

frame. The shrill noise of the noonday whistle interrupted their reveries; together they retired to a grassy
spot to share pork pies from their lunch pails and dream
dreams. In a few moments Avid fell into a deep dream-
less sleep whilst Flowers brushed the swarms of flies
from her head and studied the *Harvard Classics*, with
which he was improving himself in his spare time.

The witching hour was striking one that night as a
hooded figure stole along the waterfront toward the secret
subterranean cavern in which the Red plotters held
nightly conclave. Disguised in the scowling black beard
and astrakhan coat of a Soviet envoy, Avid Lissner's
heart was pounding furiously. The surly guard at the
entrance of the cave eyed her suspiciously.

"Halt, give the password!" he snarled in Russian.

"Death to all bourgeois aristocrats," replied Avid in
the fluent Tartar she had mastered at school. Still suspicious, the Red undesirable attempted to bar her progress.

"One side, dog of a swine!" spat Avid, striking him
down with her riding-crop. "Is this the way you welcome
a comrade with secret dispatches from the Central Coun-
cil?" Bowing and scraping humbly, the guard fell back,
muttering to himself in an obscure Ukrainian dialect.
Gathered around a roaring fire, a score of evil-eyed, dark-
skinned Anarchists were scheming the overthrow of
U. S. supremacy. Among them Avid recognized many

notorious agitators, Single Taxers, liberal readers of the *Nation* and the *New Republic*, World War slackers and other destructive forces.

"Greetings from the Union of Socialist Soviet Republics," said Avid in deep tones, "also from the autonomous republics of Turkmenistan and Uzbekistan. Regards also from the boys in the pool room in Tobolsk. The government sends you this gift." And she laid a tractor on the sideboard. A roar of savage welcome sounded from the throats of the revolutionaries. Seating herself by the fire and swallowing a cup of hot *borscht*, or Russian beet soup, Avid looked about fiercely.

"What news from our beloved fatherland?" demanded Jake (Soviet) Gold, throwing a copy of the American Constitution on the fire.

"Everything is progressing satisfactorily," replied Avid, drawing a piece of sturgeon from her pocket and gnawing it wolfishly. "Last week we shot three traitors whom we found wearing white linen shirts, also a counter-revolutionary girl spy of seventeen who owned two pairs of silk stockings."

"And what about the *New York Times*?" queried a left-wing Socialist from the right-hand corner of the room.

"Bah! One can do nothing with them—they refuse to

be bribed," growled Avid. A chorus of hisses aimed at the *New York Times* filled the room.

"We, too, have been active," reported Kalmar and Ruby, the leaders of the central factory committee. "Last night we held elections. Comrade Ryskind was appointed Head Commissar in Charge of Clean Towels."

"You betchum life," chimed in Comrade Weitzenkorn. "We also elected comrades Oppenheimer and Mankiewicz to the firing-squad."

"In front or in back?" demanded Avid in guttural English, kissing the newly elected members of the firing-squad on both cheeks. It was a rash move, for accidentally Avid's false beard became unloosened and fell to the floor. A yell of rage went up as the plotters saw how they had been duped. In a trice Avid was securely bound and gagged. A hasty meeting of the Committee on Native-born American Spies was convened and she was sentenced to be tortured and burnt. Flaming with vodka the drunken Communists piled wood on the fire and prepared the instruments. Avid, pale but determined, surveyed them contemptuously. At last the hideous paraphernalia was ready; she could hear the hiss of the smoking irons slowly approaching her skin, nearer, nearer . . .

Suddenly the clear call of a bugle resounded from outside; the door buckled, then crumpled like matchwood under the crushing battering-ram of a squad of U. S. marines at whose head Avid dimly discerned Linwood Flowers, sabre in hand. Behind them picked units of members of the National Security League, the Boy Scouts, the Girl Guides, the D. A. R. and other patriotic organizations charged in. The discomfited Reds, mouthing coarse Slavonic oaths, were soon overpowered and removed by their courteous but firm captors to serve heavy sentences in Leavenworth.

"Yes," laughed Linwood Flowers, thoroughly enjoying Avid's astonishment as he drew a gold badge from his pocket, "none other than Abe Smolinsky, U. S. Department of Justice Operative No. 546, at your service. Jake (Soviet) Gold turned stool pigeon just in the nick of time and telephoned me. You are a brave girl."

"Oh, Jake," murmured Avid, as she snuggled in the shelter of the repentant Gold's arms, "I knew you were true blue all the time. And now promise me you won't believe any more of that nasty subversive propaganda, will you?"

"No, Avid," responded Jake in manly tones. "I have learned my lesson once and for all, and should my country need me, I am ready!" And with these words he took his flushed young intended in his arms amid the cheers of the civics class. And here, as their lips met, let us draw the kindly curtain.

Little else remains to be told. The employees of the Lissner Ball-Bearing Works, exultant at being freed from the Red menace, demanded a thirty per-cent wage cut and requested to be allowed to work eleven hours a day. Avid and Jake were married and shortly afterward were found murdered in their beds. Luckily, no clues to this ghastly affair were ever found; and it is still spoken of by old-timers as "that suspicious occurrence up at Lissner's."

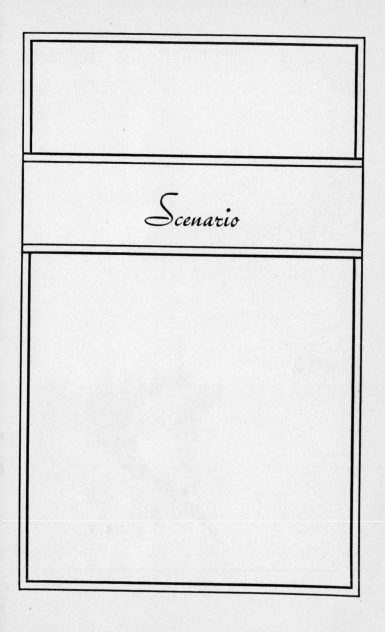

Scenario

*J*ADE in, exterior grassy knoll, long shot. Above the scene the thundering measures of Von Suppe's "Light Cavalry Overture." Austerlitz? The Plains of Abraham? Vicksburg? The Little Big Horn? Cambrai? Steady on, old son; it is Yorktown. Under a blood-red setting sun yon proud crest is Cornwallis. Blood and 'ouns, proud sirrah, dost brush so lightly past an exciseman of the Crown? Lady Rotogravure's powdered shoulders shrank from the highwayman's caress; what, Jermyn, footpads on Hounslow Heath? A certain party in the D. A.'s office will hear of this, you bastard. There was a silken insolence in his smile as he drew the great-coat about his face and leveled his shooting-iron at her dainty puss. Leave go that lady or I'll smear yuh. No quarter, eh? Me, whose ancestors scuttled stately India merchantmen of their comfits and silken stuffs and careened their piratical craft in the Dry Tortugas to carouse with bumboat women till the cock crew? Yuh'll buy my booze or I'll give yuh a handful of clouds. Me, whose ancestors rode with Yancey, Jeb Stuart, and Joe Johnston through the dusty bottoms of the Chickamauga? Oceans of love, but not one cent for tribute. Make a heel out of a guy whose grandsire, Olaf Hasholem, swapped powder and ball with the murderous Sioux through the wheels of a Conestoga wagon, who mined the yellow dirt with Sutter and slapped nuggets across the rude bars of Leadville and Goldfield? One side, damn your black hide, suh, or Ah'll send one mo' dirty Litvak to the boneyard. It's right up the exhibitor's alley, Mr. Biberman, and you got to hand it to them on a platter steaming hot. I know, Stanley, but let's look at this thing reasonable; we been showing the public Folly Larrabee's drawers two years and they been cooling off. Jeez Crize—it's a hisTORical drama, Mr. Biberman, it'll blow 'em outa the back of the houses, it's the greatest thing in the industry, it's dynamite! Pardon me, officer, is that General Washington? Bless yez little heart, mum, and who may yez be, savin' yer prisince? Honest old Brigid the apple-woman of Trinity, is it? How dégagé he sits on his charger, flicking an infinitesimal speck of ash from his plum-colored waistcoat! Gentlemen, I give you Martha Custis, hetman of the Don Cossacks, her features etched with the fragile beauty of a cameo. And I walked right in on her before she had a chance to pull the god-damned kimono together. But to be away from all this—to lean back puffing on one's churchwarden at Mount Vernon amid the dull glint of pewter, to watch the firelight playing over polished Duncan Phyfe and Adam while faithful old Cudjo cackles his ebony features and mixes a steaming lime toddy! Tired, Roy, I'm tired, I tell you. Tired of the rain, the eternal surge of the breakers on that lagoon, the glitter of the reef in that eternity out there. CHRISTIAN! She laughed contemptuously, her voluptuous throat filling with a rising sob as she faced Davidson like a hounded animal. You drove me out of Papeete but I'll go to Thursday Island with my banjo on my knee. Yeh, yeh, so what? We made FOUR pictures like that last year. Oh, my God, Mr. Biberman, give me a chance, it's only a flashback to plant that she's a woman with a past. Sixteen hundred a week I pay you to hand me back the plot of *Love's Counterfeiters* Selig made in 1912! She's who? She's what? What's the idea her coming here? What's she trying to do, turn a production office into a whorehouse? No, Miss Reznick, tell her to wait, I'll be through in five minutes. Now get it, Mr. Biberman, it's big. You establish the messroom and truck with Farnsworth till he faces Charteris. I said Sixth Rajputana Rifles and I

don't want a lotta muggs paradin' around in the uni-
forms of the Preobazhensky Guard, y' get me? Yep, he's
on a tear, those foreign directors are very temperamental,
did I ever tell you about the time Lazlo Nugasi said he'd
buy me a brassiere if I let him put it on? Fake it with a
transparency of Khyber Pass. Now an overhead shot of the
dusty tired column filing into Sidi-bel-Abbes. Shoulder
by shoulder they march in the faded blue of the Legion,
fun-loving Dick and serious-minded Tom. Buddies, the
greatest word in the French language, flying to the defense of each other like a homo pigeon. Greater love
hath Onan. Swinging a chair into that mob of lime-
juicers in the Mile End Bar in Shanghai. But came a
slant-eyed Chinese adventuress, and then? Don't shoot,
Butch, for Gossake! Heave 'em into the prison yard, we'll
keep the screws out of the cell-block and wilderness were
paradise enow. Stow the swag in Cincy, kid, and go on
alone, I'm done for. Too late, old Pogo the clown
stopped it in the sweetbreads. They buried him outside
the town that night, a motley crew of freaks and circus
people. What a sequence! Old man Klingspiel told me
he bawled like a baby. Laugh, you inhuman monster
they call the crowd, old Pogo lies dead with only a bare-
back rider's spangle to mark his grave and a seat for
every child in the public schools! When tall ships shook
out their plumage and raced from Salem to Hong Kong

to bring back tea. Break out the Black Ball ensign, Mr. Exhibitor, there's sweet music in that ole cash register! A double truck in every paper in town and a smashing drawing by the best artist we got, mind you. Take the kiddies to that colossal red-blooded human drama of a boy's love for his dog. This is my hunting lodge, we'll stop here and dry your things. But of course it's all right, cara mia, I'm old enough to be your father. Let me go, you beast—MOTHER! What are you doing here? I ask you confidentially, Horowitz, can't we get that dame to put on some women's clothes, a skirt or something? The fans are getting wise, all those flat-heeled shoes and men's shirts like a lumberjack. Get me Gerber in publicity, he'll dish out some crap about her happy home life. Vorkapich around the room to Dmitri's brother officers as they register consternation at the news. Good chance for some hokey bellies on comedy types. What, sir, you dare mention Alexandra Petrovna's name in a saloon? The kid takes it big and gives Diane the gloves across the pan socko. The usual satisfaction, I presume? Drawing on his gloves as a thin sneer played across his features. Yeh, a martinet and for Crisakes remember it's not a musical instrument this time. But eet ees madness, Serge! The best swordsman in St. Mary's parish, he weel run you through in a tweenkling! Oh, darling, you can't, you can't. Her hair had become undone and he plunged his face into its fragrance, unbuckling his sabre and flinging it on the bed beside them. Hurry, even now my husband is fried to the ears in a low boozing-den in Pokrovsky Street. Of course it is he, I'd know that lousy busby any-where in St. Petersburg. Shoot it two ways, you can always dub it in the sound track. She shrieks or she don't shriek, what the hell difference does it make? Told me he was going to night school at the Smolny Institute, the cur. And I believed him, thought Pyotr pityingly, survey-ing her luscious bust with greedy eyes. Never leave me, my sweet, and then bejeezus an angle shot toward the door of the General leaning against the lintel stroking his mustache. Crouching against the wall terrified yet shining-eyed as women are when men do gallant combat. Throw him your garter, Lady Aspinwall, throw your slipper, throw your lunch, but for Gawd's sake throw something! *Parry! Thrust! Touché!* Where are they all now, the old familiar faces? What a piece of business! Grabs a string of onions and swings himself up the bal-cony, fencing with the soldiers. Got you in the groin that time, General! Mine host, beaming genially, rubbing his hands and belching. Get Anderson ready with the sleigh-bells and keep that snow moving. Hit 'em all! Hotter on eighty-four, Joe Devlin! Are we up to speed? Quiet, please, we're turning! Chicago, hog-butcher to the world, yclept the Windy City. BOOZE AND BLOOD, he oughta know, running a drug store eleven years on Halstead Street. You cut to the back of the Big Fellow, then three lap dissolves of the presses—give 'em that Ufa stuff, then to the street—a newsboy, insert of the front page, the L roaring by—Kerist, it's the gutsiest thing in pictures! Call you back, chief. Never mind the Hays office, this baby is censor-proof! Call you back, chief. We'll heave the telephone through the glass door and smack her in the kisser with the grapefruit, they liked it once and they'll love it twice. Call you back, chief. The gat in the mesh-bag. A symbol, get me? Now remember, staccato. . . . A bit tight, my sweet? Marrowforth teetered back and forth on his heels, his sensitive artist's fingers caressing the first edition he loved. Item, one Hawes and Curtis dress-suit, one white tie, kindly return to Mister Dreyfus in the wardrobe department. What color do I remind you of? Purple shot with pleasure, if you ask me. Do I have to work with a lot of pimply grips giving me the bird? Papa's in the doghouse and keep up the tempo of the last scene, you looked crummy in yesterday's dailies. A warm, vivid and human story with just that touch of muff the fans demand. Three Hundred Titans Speed Westward as King Haakon Lays Egg on Shoe-String. And sad-eyed Grubnitz by the Wailing Wall demands: What will the inde exhibs do? Let 'em eat cake, we're packing 'em in with 29 Powell-Loys in 1938.

[39]

Ask Hyman Gerber of Waco, he can smell a box-office picture a mile away. In the freezing mists of dawn they gathered by the fuselages of their planes and gripped hands. But Rex Jennings of the shining eyes and the high heart never came back. Heinie got him over Chalons. I tell you it's murder to send a mere boy out in a crate like that! The god-damned production office on my neck all day. It's midsummer madness, Fiametta! You mustn't! I must! I want you! You want me? But I—I'm just a poor little slavey, and you—why, all life's ahead of you! Fame, the love of a good woman, children! And your music, Raoul! Excuse me, miss, are you Fiametta Desplains? I am Yankel Patchouli, a solicitor. Here is my card and a report of my recent urinalysis. Raoul! Raoul! Come quick! A million dollars! Now you can go to Paris and study your counterpoint! Damn my music, Fiametta, my happiness was in my own back yard all the time and I was, how you say it, one blind fool. The gingham dress and half-parted lips leaning on a broom. But why are you looking at me in that strange way, Tony? . . . Tony! I'm afraid of you! Oh . . . You utter contemptible despicable CAD. He got up nursing his jaw. Spew out your poison, you rat. You didn't know she was the morganatic wife of Prince Rupprecht, *did* you? That her affairs with men were the talk of Vienna, *did* you? That—Vanya, is this true? Bowed head, for her man. His boyish tousled head clean-cut against the twilight. Get out. *Get out.* GET OUT! Oh, mumsey, I want to die. That hooker's gotta lay off that booze, Mr. Metz, once more she comes on the set stinking and I take the next boat back to Buda-Pesth. But in a great tangled garden sits a forlorn tragic-eyed figure; the face a mask of carved ivory, the woman nobody knows—Tilly Bergstrom. What lies behind her shattered romance with Grant Snavely, idol of American flaps? Turn 'em over, you punks, I'll stay on this set till I get it right. Cheese it, de nippers! The jig is up, long live the jig—ring out the old, ring in the new. For love belongs to everyone, the best things in life are free.

Good News, Bibliophiles!

*A*LL first-edition collectors will go hot and cold when they hear that the new passenger list of the *S. S. Manhattan*, west-bound from Cherbourg to New York, is out again, packed with surprises and sly good humor. Richly bound in half Turk, the type in this edition is set in Goldfarb Old Style—neat but not Goudy, so to speak. *Passenger List* is daringly handled and developed, and from the first page to the bewildering climax on Page 24 there is not one idle moment. And yet in all those pages there is not one word to offend even the most delicate-minded reader. An ideal book for youngsters from six to sixty.

On Page 2 the action gets under way with a bang with "Information for Passengers." "An information bureau," says the author, with twinkling eyes, "has been provided for the passengers. All inquiries for information should be addressed to that office." What dry crackling wit the man has! Let us suppose that a retired wet-fly fisherman named Peckinpaugh wishes to get information. Heedless of warnings from the other passengers, he applies at the cigar-counter on C deck.

"Pardon me, I should like some information," falters Peckinpaugh.

"Some what?" demands the clerk brutally.

"Information," stammers Peckinpaugh. "There's a man been sleeping under my berth the last four nights, and every time I get up during the night for a glass of water he tickles the soles of my feet. I—I want some information about him."

Such a situation can only end in disaster, as Mr. Peckinpaugh soon finds out, for in a trice the clerk has stuffed his mouth with cigars and he is being borne off to the kitchen to be chopped up and made into curry. Just one instance among hundreds of the folly of not reading *Passenger List* carefully. Can you picture the feelings of Mrs. Peckinpaugh and her children when they wait for Mr. Peckinpaugh at the pier and instead meet a curry?

At this point the love interest in *Passenger List* begins to rear its ugly head. Under the significant title "Baggage," we read: "The baggage-master will be allowed to keep one out of every twenty ripe trunks he sorts, but must not keep any green ones for himself." Nevertheless, as the story unfolds, we see a whimsical vignette of the baggage-master and his motley band of urchins sneaking cautiously into Farmer Zola's orchard and rifling it of green trunks, on which they later feast. But what is this? On Page 9 the plot suddenly takes a new turn, for here is the very meat of the tale, a breezy and intimate picture of all our fellow-passengers! Good old *Doctor Harvey P. Flug and Mrs. Flug,* not to mention *Harrison Fister* and *G. Ransom Flebworth!* And, skipping to the B's, who will ever forget that sparkling funsmith, *R. K. Bulkis and wife,* or *George M. Bayswater,* or *Miss Grace Bratcher with child?* Or do you think the years will ever efface the memory of *Celia Zinkeiser, Benj. Zemil,* and *Serge Zcjasny?* No, a thousand times no!

From now on our tale slowly but surely nears its inevitable end. In one close-packed page, 17 to 18 inclusive, we see how the barometer works and what the difference in time is between Paris and Milk City, Montana. Port and starboard, neap tides, and measuring by sound at sea all move swiftly across the scene. Then, with the suddenness of a thunder-clap, we are reading about the Gulf Stream: "Joining with the Labrador Current, it sweeps northward until it reaches the Grand Banks. Then, dividing into two portions, one branch

[47]

carries rice pudding toward the Azores and the coast of Portugal and the other roast leg of veal with *pont neuf* potatoes to the Baltic States."

The close of *Passenger List* is marred with a faint touch of melancholy, for we find that if we are ever in Malmoë, Finland, the only place to get steamship tickets is Sköppsbron 9, ring twice and ask for Denny. In Zagreb the situation is even worse, for there Lazar Temestyvo has a corner on them at 12 Prägerstrasse. And so, with the sun sinking in a blaze of glory in the west, we pace the deck, arm in arm, ever and anon letting our thoughts stray back to *Clarence J. Abel, H. B. Abernethy,* and *Professor and Mrs. Daniel Aspinwall.* Already the dinner gong is sounding and we have just time to sip an imperative before we descend to the dining-room. *Salami.*

The Idol's Eye

I HAD been week-ending with Gabriel Snubbers at his villa in Cheyne-Stokes, on the edge of the Downs. Gabriel isn't seen about as much as he used to be; one hears that an eccentric aunt left him a tidy little sum and the lazy beggar refuses to leave his native haunts. Four of us had cycled down from London together: Gossip Gabrilowitsch, the Polish pianist; Downey Couch, the Irish tenor; Frank Falcovsky, the Jewish prowler, and myself, Clay Modelling. Snubbers, his face beaming, met us at the keeper's lodge. His eyes were set in deep rolls of fat for our arrival, and I couldn't help thinking how well they looked. I wondered whether it was because his daring farce, *Mrs. Stebbins' Step-Ins*, had been doing so well at the Haymarket.

"Deuced decent of you chaps to make this filthy trip," he told us, leading us up the great avenue of two stately alms toward the house. "Rum place, this." A surprise awaited us when we reached the house, for the entire left wing had just burned down. Snubbers, poor fellow, stared at it a bit ruefully, I thought.

"Just as well, it was only a plague-spot," sympathized Falcovsky. Snubbers was thoughtful.

"D'ye know, you chaps," he said suddenly, "I could swear an aunt of mine was staying in that wing." Falcovsky stirred the ashes with his stick and uncovered a pair of knitting needles and a half-charred corset.

"No, it must have been the other wing," dismissed Snubbers. "How about a spot of whisky and soda?" We entered and Littlejohn, Snubbers' man, brought in a spot of whisky on a piece of paper which we all examined with interest. A splendid fire was already roaring in the middle of the floor to drive out the warmth.

"Soda?" offered Snubbers. I took it to please him, for Gabriel's cellar was reputedly excellent. A second later I wished that I had drunk the cellar instead. Baking soda is hardly the thing after a three-hour bicycle trip.

"You drank that like a little soldier," he complimented, his little button eyes fastened on me. I was about to remark that I had never drunk a little soldier, when I noticed Littlejohn hovering in the doorway.

"Yes, that will be all," Snubbers waved, "and, oh, by the way, send up to London tomorrow for a new wing, will you?" Littlejohn bowed and left, silently, sleekly Oriental.

"Queer cove, Littlejohn," commented Snubbers. "Shall I tell you a story?" He did, and it was one of the dullest I have ever heard. At the end of it Falcovsky grunted. Snubbers surveyed him suspiciously.

"Why, what's up, old man?" he queried.

"What's up? Nothing's up," snarled Falcovsky. "Can't a man grunt in front of an open fire if he wants to?"

"But . . ." began Snubbers.

"But nothing," Falcovsky ground. "You haven't lived till you've grunted in front of an open fire. Just for that— grunt, grunt, grunt," and he grunted several times out of sheer spite. None of us dared remonstrate, for Falcovsky was reputedly the owner of great natural beds of Eskimo pies and would pay through the nose to keep his name free from scandal. The last was no idle boast—Falcovsky's was the only nose in England I have ever seen large enough to pay through, and had the Bank of England ever needed him, he could have made his fortune as a cashier's wicket.

"It's a funny thing," brooded Snubbers.

"Oh, it is, is it?" flared Falcovsky, throwing himself on Snubbers. We tore them apart and only ended the dispute by measuring the former's nose against Snubbers'. Of course Falcovsky won hands down—that is, hands down on his nose—and we resumed our drinking. The baking soda was beginning to tell on Snubbers.

"Remarkable thing happened the other day," he began. "I was pottering about in the garden . . ."

"Why must one always potter around in a garden?" demanded Couch. "Can't you potter around in an arm-chair just as well?"

"I did once," confessed Snubbers moodily, revealing a whitish scar on his chin. "Gad, sir, what a tigress she was!" He chewed his wad of carbon paper reminiscently. "Oh, well, never mind. But as I was saying—I was going through some of my great-grandfather's things the other day . . ."

"What things?" demanded Falcovsky, whose nose was beginning to heal.

"His bones, if you must know," Snubbers said coldly. "You know, Great-grandfather died under strange cir-cumstances. He opened a vein in his bath."

"I never knew baths had veins," protested Gabril-owitsch.

"I never knew his great-grandfather had a ba—" began Falcovsky derisively. With a shout Snubbers threw him-self on Falcovsky. It was the signal for Pandemonium, the upstairs girl, to enter and throw herself with a shout on Couch. The outcome of the necking bee was as fol-lows: Canadians 12, Visitors 9. Krebs and Vronsky

played footie, subbing for Gerber and Weinwald, who
were disabled by flying antipasto.

We were silent after Snubbers had spoken; men who
have wandered in far places have an innate delicacy about
their great-grandfathers' bones. Snubbers' face was a
mask, his voice a harsh whip of pain in the stillness when
he spoke again.

"I fancy none of you knew my great-grandfather," he
said slowly. "Before your time, I daresay. A rare giant
of a man with quizzical eyes and a great shock of wiry
red hair, he had come through the Peninsular Wars
without a scratch. Women loved this impetual Irish ad-
venturer who would rather fight than eat and vice versa.
The wars over, he turned toward cookery, planning to
devote his failing years to the perfection of the welsh
rarebit, a dish he loved. One night he was chaffing at
The Bit, a tavern in Portsmouth, when he overheard a
chance remark from a brawny gunner's mate in his cups.
In Calcutta the man had heard native tales of a mysterious idol, whose single eye was a flawless ruby.

" 'Topscuttle my bamberger, it's the size of a bloomin'
pigeon's egg!' spat the salt, shifting his quid to his other
cheek. 'A bloomin' rajah's ransom and ye may lay to that,
mateys!'

"The following morning the *Maid of Hull*, a frigate
of the line mounting thirty-six guns, out of Bath and

into bed in a twinkling, dropped downstream on the tide, bound out for Bombay, object matrimony. On her as passenger went my great-grandfather, an extra pair of nankeen pants his only baggage and a dirk in his throat ready for use. Fifty-three days later in Poona, he was heading for the interior of one of the Northern states. Living almost entirely on cameo brooches and the few ptarmigan which fell to the ptrigger of his pfowling-piece, he at last sighted the towers of Ishpeming, the Holy City of the Surds and Cosines, fanatic Moham-medan warrior sects. He disguised himself as a beggar and entered the gates.

"For weeks my great-grandfather awaited his chance to enter the temple of the idol. They were changing the guard one evening when he saw it. One of the native janissaries dropped his knife. My great-grandfather leaped forward with cringing servility and returned it to him, in the small of his back. Donning the soldier's turban, he quickly slipped into his place. Midnight found him within ten feet of his prize. Now came the final test. He furtively drew from the folds of his robes a plate of curry, a dish much prized by Indians, and set it in a far corner. The guards rushed upon it with bulging squeals of delight. A twist of his wrist and the gem was his. With an elaborately stifled yawn, my great-grand-father left under pretense of going out for a glass of water. The soldiers winked slyly but when he did not return after two hours, their suspicions were aroused. They hastily made a canvass of the places where water was served and their worst fears were realized. The ruby in his burnoose, Great-grandfather was escaping by fast elephant over the Khyber Pass. Dockside loungers in Yarmouth forty days later stared curiously at a mammoth of a man with flaming red hair striding abstractedly toward the Bull and Bloater Tavern. Under his belt lay the Ruby Eye.

"Ten years to that night had passed, and my great-grandfather, in seclusion under this very roof, had almost forgotten his daring escapade. Smoking by the fireplace, he listened to the roar of the wind and reviewed his campaigns. Suddenly he leaped to his feet—a dark face had vanished from the window. Too late my great-grandfather snatched up powder and ball and sent a charge of grape from his dueling-pistol hurtling into the night. The note pinned to the window drained the blood from his face.

"It was the first of a series. Overnight his hair turned from rose-red to snow-white. And finally, when it seemed as though madness were to rob them of their revenge, they came."

Snubbers stopped, his eyes those of a man who had looked beyond life and had seen things best left hidden

[57]

from mortal orbs. Falcovsky's hand was trembling as he pressed a pinch of snuff against his gums.

"You—you mean?" he quavelled.

"Yes." Snubbers' voice had sunk to a whisper. "He fought with the strength of nine devils, but the movers took away his piano. You see," he added very gently, "Great-grandfather had missed the last four instalments." Gabrilowitsch sighed deeply and arose, his eyes fixed intently on Snubbers.

"And—and the ruby?" he asked softly, his delicate fingers closing around the fire-tongs.

"Oh, *that*," shrugged Snubbers, "I just threw that in to make it interesting."

We bashed in the top of his conk and left him to the vultures.

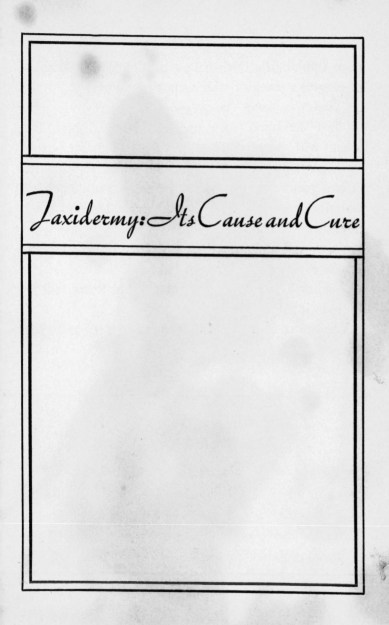

Taxidermy: Its Cause and Cure

$\mathcal{A}$ CERTAIN party pretty high up in the American News Company whom we will call Mr. X (Mr. X my foot, it's a good deal more like Timberg, if the truth be told) has recently run across an astonishing thing. During the past month hordes of commuters have been bothering the newsstands for books on taxidermy, leaving a small deposit, and never returning to claim the books. After eleven million dollars in deposits had accumulated in this fashion, Mr. Timberg naturally got worried and went to a certain party pretty high up in the District Attorney's office (a Mr. $\dfrac{X^2 - Y^2}{b}$). They finally arrived at the only plausible solution; viz., that an international ring of people totally uninterested in taxidermy has been operating in the East. And there the matter rests. The eleven million dollars is still waiting for anybody who wants it.

Whence comes this sudden revival of uninterest in taxidermy? (Or perhaps "revival of interest in untaxidermy" would be better. On the other hand, "unrevival of interest in non-taxidermy" comes closer to it . . . ugh, that cummings man will drive Me c(raz)y . . .) Everywhere one goes these days, the mere mention of taxidermy is followed by flaccid muscles and complete lassitude. In one case I know of, a man put a whole castle, thoroughly equipped with flambeaux, lusty trenchermen, and a beautiful princess, to sleep for a hundred years by just pulling out a handbook on taxidermy. The answer becomes clear in W. P. Manton's *Taxidermy Without a Teacher* (Lothrop, Lee & Shepard, 1882). After perusing this little volume, the first impulse is to run out and buy a taxidermist outfit just for the pleasure of throwing it away. And right here is where the tyro runs into trouble. In his eagerness to throw away taxidermy outfits, he buys shoddy and gimcrack materials, and then wonders why he gets no pleasure out of throwing them away. Any good sporting-goods store can supply you with a first-class throw-away taxidermy outfit for a small fortune. The handy boy with a workshop in his cellar can whip together a sturdy outfit if only he avoids Mr. Manton's book carefully enough.

TAXIDERMY: ITS CAUSE AND CURE

The first thing to discard in taxidermy is a serviceable hunting suit made of waterproof corduroy. This is made by pegging fifteen or twenty yards of corduroy to the floor and crawling under it. Snip this to fit the outline of your body, cut a hole for the face, and throw away. It is a good plan to have a whistle or a bugle nearby in case you are unable to cut your way out from under the corduroy. One little fellow I knew forgot this detail and his family was in the laughable position of having to throw away the taxidermist instead of his outfit when they finally found him. In his dreamy way, Mr. Manton says, "The coat of a collecting suit should be a mere succession of pockets." Frankly, the only result I obtained by sewing together four or five hundred pockets was paranoia and a coat that swelled like a sponge whenever I was caught in a thunderstorm.

Unfortunately, although he urges every taxidermist to take a box lunch into the field, Mr. Manton gives us no hint as to its contents. "Tramping on an empty stomach," he points out, "will almost always upset one for the whole day." I have tramped on the empty stomachs of innumerable friends to test this statement but I cannot report ever having been upset. On the contrary, I experienced a warm and delicious sensation, something like coffee. In fact, I had it analyzed later and it was coffee. So much for Mr. Manton and his aversion to coffee.

Personally, I have always found coffee ideal for stimulating brain fag and I should like to remark in passing that it is men of Mr. Manton's stripe who are raising hob with our personal liberties. I like coffee, I like tea, I like the girls and the girls like me, and I see no reason why an old lady with an umbrella should drive us out of the park for a little innocent spooning. A pretty kettle of fish indeed when you can't even take your sheba for a ride in the town jitney without some copper's nark nosing in on you. Bad 'cess to the shpalpeens, wurra wurra.

Now that you have collected your complete outfit, the best thing is to bake it in a pie or wrap it in a package resembling an innocent loaf of bread and take the trolley all the way to the car barn. The motormen usually step out for a bite around five-fifteen, leaving only Mr. Cleary, so just hide your "loaf of bread" (taxidermy outfit) somewhere in the shadows and set fire to the car barn. If, after that, you should *still* want to practise taxidermy, start in by mounting a tiger. Wrap your arms firmly around his neck and ride away. Do anything you want, only get out of this room. Mamma's neuralgia is bothering her something terrible.

Strictly from Hunger

*Y*ES, I was excited, and small wonder. What boy wouldn't be, boarding a huge, mysterious, puffing steam train for golden California? As Mamma adjusted my reefer and strapped on my leggings, I almost burst with impatience. Grinning redcaps lifted my luggage into the compartment and spat on it. Mamma began to weep silently into a small pillow-case she had brought along for the purpose.

"Oh, son, I wish you hadn't become a scenario writer!" she sniffled.

"Aw, now, Moms," I comforted her, "it's no worse than playing the piano in a call-house." She essayed a brave little smile, and, reaching into her reticule, produced a flat package which she pressed into my hands. For a moment I was puzzled, then I cried out with glee.

"Jelly sandwiches! Oh, Moms!"

"Eat them all, boy o' mine," she told me, "they're good for boys with hollow little legs." Tenderly she pinned to my lapel the green tag reading "To Plushnick Productions, Hollywood, California." The whistle shrilled and in a moment I was chugging out of Grand Central's dreaming spires followed only by the anguished cries of relatives who would now have to go to work. I had chugged only a few feet when I realized that I had left without the train, so I had to run back and wait for it to start.

As we sped along the glorious fever spots of the Hudson I decided to make a tour of inspection. To my surprise I found that I was in the only passenger car of the train; the other cars were simply dummies snipped out of cardboard and painted to simulate coaches. Even "passengers" had been cunningly drawn in colored crayons in the "window," as well as ragged tramps clinging to the blinds below and drinking Jamaica ginger. With a rueful smile I returned to my seat and gorged myself on jelly sandwiches.

At Buffalo the two other passengers and I discovered to our horror that the conductor had been left behind. We finally decided to divide up his duties; I punched the tickets, the old lady opposite me wore a conductor's hat and locked the washroom as we came into stations, and the young man who looked as if his feet were not mates consulted a Hamilton watch frequently. But we missed the conductor's earthy conversation and it was not until we had exchanged several questionable stories that we began to forget our loss.

A flicker of interest served to shorten the trip. At Fort Snodgrass, Ohio, two young and extremely polite road-agents boarded the train and rifled us of our belongings. They explained that they were modern Robin Hoods and were stealing from the poor to give to the rich. They had intended to rape all the women and depart for Sherwood Forest, but when I told them that it was in England, their chagrin was comical in the extreme. They declined my invitation to stay and take a chance on the train's pool, declaring that the engineer had fixed the run and would fleece us, and got off at South Bend with every good wish.

The weather is always capricious in the Middle West, and although it was midsummer, the worst blizzard in Chicago's history greeted us on our arrival. The streets were crowded with thousands of newsreel cameramen trying to photograph one another bucking the storm on the Lake Front. It was a novel idea for the newsreels and I wished them well. With only two hours in Chicago I would be unable to see the city, and the thought drew me into a state of composure. I noted with pleasure that a fresh coat of grime had been given to the Dearborn Street station, though I was hardly vain enough to believe that it had anything to do with my visit. There was the usual ten-minute wait while the porters withdrew with my portable typewriter to a side room and flailed it with hammers, and at last I was aboard the "Sachem," crack train of the B.B.D. & O. lines.

It was as if I had suddenly been transported into another world. "General Crook," in whom I was to make my home for the next three days, and his two neighbors, "Lake Tahoe" and "Chief Malomai," were everything that the word "Pullman" implies; they were Pullmans. Uncle Eben, the dusky Ethiopian in charge of "General Crook," informed me that the experiment of air-cooling the cars had been so successful that the road intended trying to heat them next winter.

"Ah suttinly looks fo'd to dem roastin' ears Ah's gwine have next winter, he, he, he!" he chuckled, rubbing soot into my hat.

The conductor told me he had been riding on trains for so long that he had begun to smell like one, and sure enough, two brakemen waved their lanterns at him that night and tried to tempt him down a siding in Kansas City. We became good friends and it came as something of a blow when I heard the next morning that he had fallen off the train during the night. The fireman said that we had circled about for an hour trying to find him but that it had been impossible to lower a boat because we did not carry a boat.

The run was marked by only one incident out of the ordinary. I had ordered breaded veal cutlet the first evening, and my waiter, poking his head into the kitchen, had repeated the order. The cook, unfortunately, understood him to say "*dreaded* veal cutlet," and resenting the slur, sprang at the waiter with drawn razor. In a few seconds I was the only living remnant of the shambles, and at Topeka I was compelled to wait until a new shambles was hooked on and I proceeded with dinner.

It seemed only a scant week or ten days before we were pulling into Los Angeles. I had grown so attached to my porter that I made him give me a lock of his hair. I wonder if he still has the ten-cent piece I gave him? There was a gleam in his eye which could only have been insanity as he leaned over me. Ah, Uncle Eben, faithful old retainer, where are you now? Gone to what obscure boneyard? If this should chance to meet your kindly gaze, drop me a line care of the Railroad Men's Y.M.C.A. at Gloucester, Mass. They know what to do with it.

[71]

— II —

The violet hush of twilight was descending over Los Angeles as my hostess, Violet Hush, and I left its suburbs headed toward Hollywood. In the distance a glow of huge piles of burning motion-picture scripts lit up the sky. The crisp tang of frying writers and directors whetted my appetite. How good it was to be alive, I thought, inhaling deep lungfuls of carbon monoxide. Suddenly our powerful Gatti-Cazazza slid to a stop in the traffic.

"What is it, Jenkin?" Violet called anxiously through the speaking-tube to the chauffeur (played by Lyle Talbot).

A *suttee* was in progress by the roadside, he said—did we wish to see it? Quickly Violet and I elbowed our way through the crowd. An enormous funeral pyre composed of thousands of feet of film and scripts, drenched with Chanel Number Five, awaited the torch of Jack Holt, who was to act as master of ceremonies. In a few terse words Violet explained this unusual custom borrowed from the Hindus and never paid for. The worst disgrace that can befall a producer is an unkind notice from a New York reviewer. When this happens, the producer becomes a pariah in Hollywood. He is shunned by his friends, thrown into bankruptcy, and like a Japanese electing hara-kiri, he commits *suttee*. A great bonfire is made of the film and the luckless producer, followed by directors, actors, technicians, and the producer's wives, immolate themselves. Only the scenario writers are exempt. These are tied between the tails of two spirited Caucasian ponies, which are then driven off in opposite directions. This custom is called "a conference."

Violet and I watched the scene breathlessly. Near us Harry Cohn, head of Columbia Studios, was being rubbed with huck towels preparatory to throwing himself into the flames. He was nonchalantly smoking a Rocky Ford five-center, and the man's courage drew a tear to the eye of even the most callous. Weeping relatives besought him to eschew his design, but he stood adamant. Adamant Eve, his plucky secretary, was being rubbed with crash towels preparatory to flinging herself into Cohn's embers. Assistant directors busily prepared spears, war-bonnets and bags of pemmican which the Great Chief would need on his trip to the "Happy Hunting Grounds." Wampas and beads to placate the Great Spirit (played by Will Hays) were piled high about the stoical tribesman.

Suddenly Jack Holt (played by Edmund Lowe) raised his hand for silence. The moment had come. With bowed head Holt made a simple invocation couched in one-syllable words so that even the executives might understand. Throwing his five-center to a group of autograph-hunters, the great man poised himself for the fatal leap. But from off-scene came the strident clatter of cocoanut shells, and John Mosher, Filmdom's fearless critic, wearing the uniform of a Confederate guerrilla and the whiskers of General Beauregard, galloped in on a foam-flecked pinto. It was he whose mocking review had sent Cohn into Coventry. It was a dramatic moment as the two stood pitted against each other—Cohn against Mosher, the Blue against the Gray. But with true Southern gallantry Mosher was the first to extend the hand of friendship.

"Ah reckon it was an unworthy slur, suh," he said in manly tones. "Ah-all thought you-all's pictuah was lousy but it opened at the Rialto to sensational grosses, an' Ah-all 'pologizes. Heah, have a yam." And he drew a yam from his tunic. Not to be outdone in hospitality, Cohn drew a yam from his tunic, and soon they were exchanging yams and laughing over the old days.

When Violet and I finally stole away to our waiting motor, we felt that we were somehow nearer to each other. I snuggled luxuriously into the buffalo lap-robe Violet had provided against the treacherous night air and gazed out at the gleaming neon lights. Soon we would be in Beverly Hills, and already the quaint native women were swarming alongside in their punts urging us to buy their cunning beadwork and mangoes. Occasionally I threw a handful of coppers to the Negro boys, who dove for them joyfully. The innocent squeals of the policemen as the small blackamoors pinched them were irresistible. Unable to resist them, Violet and I were soon pinching each other till our skins glowed. Violet was good to the touch, with a firm fleshy texture like a winesap or pippin. It seemed but a moment before we were sliding under the porte-cochère of her home, a magnificent rambling structure of beaverboard patterned after an Italian ropewalk of the sixteenth century. It had recently been remodeled by a family of wrens who had introduced chewing-gum into the left wing, and only three or four obscure Saxon words could do it justice.

I was barely warming my hands in front of the fire and watching Lloyd Pantages turn on a spit when my presence on the Pacific Slope made itself felt. The news of my arrival had thrown international financial centers into an uproar, and sheaves of wires, cables, phone messages, and even corn began piling up. An ugly rumor that I might reorganize the motion-picture industry was being bruited about in the world's commodity markets. My brokers, Whitelipped & Trembling, were beside themselves. The Paris Bourse was begging them for assurances of stability and Threadneedle Street awaited my next move with drumming pulses. Film shares ricocheted sharply, although wools and meats were sluggish, if not downright sullen. To the reporters who flocked around me I laughingly disclaimed that this was a business trip. I was simply a scenario writer to whom the idea of work was abhorrent. A few words murmured into the transatlantic telephone, the lift of an eyebrow here, the shrug of a shoulder there, and equilibrium was soon restored. I washed sparsely, curled my mustache with a heated hairpin, flicked a drop of Sheik Lure on my lapel, and rejoined my hostess.

After a copious dinner, melting-eyed beauties in lacy black underthings fought with each other to serve me kümmel. A hurried apology, and I was curled up in bed with the Autumn, 1927, issue of *The Yale Review*. Halfway through an exciting synthesis on Sir Thomas Aquinas' indebtedness to Professors Whitehead and Spengler, I suddenly detected a stowaway blonde under the bed. Turning a deaf ear to her heartrending entreaties and burning glances, I sent her packing. Then I treated my face to a feast of skin food, buried my seepy head in the pillow and went bye-bye.

– III –

Hollywood Boulevard! I rolled the rich syllables over on my tongue and thirstily drank in the beauty of the scene before me. On all sides nattily attired boulevardiers clad in rich stuffs strolled nonchalantly, inhaling cubebs and exchanging epigrams stolen from Martial and Wilde. Thousands of scantily draped but none the less appetizing extra girls milled past me, their mouths a scarlet wound and their eyes clearly defined in their faces. Their voluptuous curves set my blood on fire, and as I made my way down Mammary Lane, a strange thought began to invade my brain: I realized that I had not eaten breakfast yet. In a Chinese eatery cunningly built in the shape of an old shoe I managed to assuage the inner man with a chopped glove salad topped off with frosted cocoa. Charming platinum-haired hostesses in red pajamas and peaked caps added a note of color to the surroundings, whilst a gypsy orchestra played selections from Victor Herbert's operettas on musical saws. It was a bit of old Vienna come to life, and the sun was a red ball in the heavens before I realized with a start that I had promised to report at the Plushnick Studios.

Commandeering a taxicab, I arrived at the studio just in time to witness the impressive ceremony of changing the guard. In the central parade ground, on a snowy white charger, sat Max Plushnick, resplendent in a producer's uniform, his chest glittering with first mortgage liens, amortizations, and estoppals. His personal guard, composed of picked vice-presidents of the Chase National Bank, was drawn up stiffly about him in a hollow square. But the occasion was not a happy one. A writer had been caught trying to create an adult picture.

The drums rolled dismally, and the writer, his head sunk on his chest, was led out amid a ghastly silence. With the aid of a small stepladder Plushnick slid lightly from his steed. Sternly he ripped the epaulets and buttons from the traitor's tunic, broke his sword across his knee, and in a few harsh words demoted him to the mail department.

"And now," began Plushnick, "I further condemn you to eat . . ."

"No, no!" screamed the poor wretch, falling to his knees and embracing the general's same, "not that, not that!"

"Stand up, man," ordered Plushnick, his lip curling, "I condemn you to eat in the studio restaurant for ten days and may God have mercy on your soul." The awful words rang out on the still evening air and even Plushnick's hardened old mercenaries shuddered. The heartrending cries of the unfortunate were drowned in the boom of the sunset gun.

In the wardrobe department I was photographed, fingerprinted, and measured for the smock and Windsor tie which was to be my uniform. A nameless fear clutched at my heart as two impassive turnkeys herded me down a corridor to my supervisor's office. For what seemed hours we waited in an anteroom. Then my serial number was called, the leg-irons were struck off, and I was shoved through a door into the presence of Diana ffrench-Mamoulian.

How to describe what followed? Diana ffrench-Mamoulian was accustomed to having her way with writers, and my long lashes and peachblow mouth seemed to whip her to insensate desire. In vain, time and again, I tried to bring her attention back to the story we were discussing, only to find her gem-incrusted fingers straying through my hair. When our interview was over, her cynical attempt to "date me up" made every fiber of my being cry out in revolt.

"P-please," I stammered, my face burning, "I—I wish you wouldn't. . . . I'm engaged to a Tri Kappa at Goucher—"

"Just one kiss," she pleaded, her breath hot against my

neck. In desperation I granted her boon, knowing full well that my weak defences were crumbling before the onslaught of this love tigree. Finally she allowed me to leave, but only after I had promised to dine at her penthouse apartment and have an intimate chat about the script. The basket of slave bracelets and marzipan I found awaiting me on my return home made me realize to what lengths Diana would go.

I was radiant that night in blue velvet tails and a boutonniere of diamonds from Cartier's, my eyes starry and the merest hint of cologne at my ear-lobes. An inscrutable Oriental served the Lucullan repast and my vis-à-vis was as effervescent as the wine.

"Have a bit of the wing, darling?" queried Diana solicitously, indicating the roast Long Island airplane with applesauce. I tried to turn our conversation from the personal note, but Diana would have none of it. Soon we were exchanging gay bantam over the mellow Vouvray, laughing as we dipped fastidious fingers into the Crisco parfait for which Diana was famous. Our meal finished, we sauntered into the play-room and Diana turned on the radio. With a savage snarl the radio turned on her and we slid over the waxed floor in the intricate maze of the jackdaw strut. Without quite knowing why, I found myself hesitating before the plate of liqueur candies Diana was pressing on me.

"I don't think I should—really I'm a trifle faint—"

"Oh, come on," she urged masterfully. "After all, you're old enough to be your father—I mean I'm old enough to be my mother. . . ." She stuffed a brandy bon-bon between my clenched teeth. Before long I was eating them thirstily, reeling about the room and shouting snatches of coarse drunken doggerel. My brain was on fire, I tell you. Through the haze I saw Diana ffrench-Mamoulian, her nostrils dilated, groping for me. My scream of terror only egged her on, overturning chairs and tables in her bestial pursuit. With superhuman talons she tore off my collar and suspenders. I sank to my knees, choked with sobs, hanging on to my last shirt-stud like a drowning man. Her Svengali eyes were slowly hypnotizing me; I fought like a wounded bird—and then, blissful unconsciousness.

When I came to, the Oriental servant and Diana were battling in the center of the floor. As I watched, Yen Shee Gow drove a well-aimed blow to her mid-section, following it with a right cross to the jaw. Diana staggered and rolled under a table. Before my astonished eyes John Chinaman stripped the mask from his face and revealed the features of Blanche Almonds, a little seamstress I had long wooed unsuccessfully in New York. Gently she bathed my temples with Florida water and explained how she had followed me, suspecting Diana ffrench-Mamoulian's intentions. I let her rain kisses over my face and lay back in her arms as beaming Ivan tucked us in and cracked his whip over the prancing bays. In a few seconds our sleigh was skimming over the hard crust toward Port Arthur and freedom, leaving Plushnick's discomfited officers gnashing one another's teeth. The wintry Siberian moon glowed over the tundras, drenching my hair with moonbeams for Blanche to kiss away. And so, across the silvery steppes amid the howling of wolves, we rode into a new destiny, purified in the crucible that men call Hollywood.

Poisonous Mushrooms

OR

ARE WE AT THE CROSSROADS?

*N*OW that autumn is here again, every Tom, Dick, and Harry will be waking up in the morning and asking himself the question "Poisonous mushrooms—yes or no?" In every mossy dell, in every nook of granny, these delicious little edibles are springing up. Only yesterday I happened to fall into conversation with a stranger in the subway, an extremely well-made woman of thirty-one with tiny hands and feet. I noticed that she was eating a small umbrella-shaped object and asked her what it was.

"An umbrella," she replied shortly, descending from the train at Seventy-second Street. Needless to say, the incident did not pass unnoticed, and I retired in confusion amid the hearty laughter of several wealthy cattle-drovers who had come down to New York for the day on the steam cars.

I first became interested in mushrooms about ten years ago. Two friends of mine named Johnny had a little place, a sort of cellar, on Fifty-second Street where they kept coal and wood and ice. I was down there one evening bent on some coal and wood when Tony pointed to the ceiling and said "*Corpo di Bacco,* what's *that?*" I looked up and there was a whole clump of mushrooms growing right out at me. Well, I let out a scream fit to wake a dead man—as a matter of fact, it *did* wake up a dead man who'd been in the corner for three days and he came over and tried to bite me. As I say, I was in bed nearly two weeks that time, but after I was well, I got this Frank and Johnny to put aside the place as a sort of permanent laboratory where I could study the mushrooms.

It will probably come as a mild shock to no one that there are all of four hundred different kinds of mushrooms. Four hundred and one, really, because when I looked up this fact in the *World Almanac,* I found a new variety growing out of Page 29. On closer examination it turned out to be a piece of old bread—a more fortunate find than I thought, for I eventually sold it to a lady who was furnishing a house on L––g I––––d and needed a piece of bread to go with her Jacobean furniture. Any mushroom-fancier will be able to tell you a hundred similar stories, which is a good reason for keeping away from mushroom-fanciers.

Now what are mushrooms? Nothing more or less than toadstools, though why they are called toadstools is beyond me; I have yet to see a toad sitting on a stool, although I have combed all the books dealing with the subject. Of course I haven't had a chance to read the books yet—all I've been able to do is comb them, but still, it seems a peculiar name to give an unoffending mushroom, doesn't it? It was probably made up by someone who hated mushrooms and thought he could get even. But why should anybody hate mushrooms? The little fellow goes about his business quietly; once in a while he kills a family of twenty or thirty people, but then, what right has anyone to have a family of twenty or thirty people? I was wrapping up some laundry in a newspaper recently and saw a note about a man who had had thirty children. This sort of thing can't go on indefinitely, no matter what the man says.

In the eleven years I have been studying mushrooms at First Hand, my laboratory on Fifty-second Street, I have seen cases of almost uncanny intelligence among my specimens. I had a Peppery Lactarius growing in a glass right next to a Fistulina Hepatica, or Beefsteak Mushroom. (If you can imagine a purple beefsteak covered with short prickly spines growing out of a tree, you will easily see why science chose this name, and you can then explain it to me.) Well, one morning I made the rounds of my collection and found that during the night Miss Peppery Lactarius had moved into Mr. Beefsteak Mushroom's jar. I woke up my assistant, put a little ice on his head, and quizzed him. But no; he had been right there on the floor since eleven-thirty the night before. To this day we have never been able to solve the riddle, and it is still referred to by superstitious folk in the neighborhood as "The Mystery of the Migrating Mushrooms." I am thinking of bringing it out in book form, perhaps adding a mysterious puffy toadstool in a black hat who was seen skulking near by.

But how to tell the poisonous mushroom from the harmless variety, since both are found in the same localities, have the same habits, and the same dull look around the face? Ah—don't be surprised—the mushroom *has* a face, and if you look very closely and carefully, you will see the merest hint of an eye, two noses, and a lip. Getting back to how you are to tell the poisonous variety from the harmless, we have what we call the Alfred Zeigler test, named after Professor Schaffner of the University of Rochester. The mushrooms are boiled for twenty minutes and their jackets removed. They are then placed in a frying pan with a cubic centimetre of butter, a gram of pepper, and a penny-weight of coarse salt, after which they are subjected to 137 degrees of heat Fahrenheit in the laboratory oven, removed, and placed on antiseptic paper plates. Fifteen minutes after they are eaten, a reaction will be noted. If the mushrooms are harmless, the subject will want to lie down, remove his collar, and roll over on his or her face. If poisonous, the balance of the mushrooms should be thrown out, as they are unfit to consume.

The mushroom often turns up in some really remarkable forms. Sir Joseph Mushroom, from whom their name is derived, tells an interesting anecdote. A cask of wine had been left undisturbed in a cellar for three years, in some country other than the United States. At the end of that time, the cask was found firmly fastened to the ceiling by a large mushroom which had grown as the wine leaked out. The cask was quite empty when found, and how the mushroom looked was nobody's business. Sir Joseph, by the way, no longer raises mushrooms; he has settled down quietly in Surrey, where he devotes himself to raising bees, but there is still a reminiscent gleam in his eye when Professor Moriarty is mentioned.

Little else remains to be told. Fred Patton, the former Erie train boy, still continues to rise in Mr. Raskolnikov's mercantile establishment on Ann Street, and Gloria Raskolnikov blushes prettily whenever Fred's name is uttered. This, however, is all too seldom, as the unfortunate Fred was hit in the vertical cervix by a baked apple last New Year's Day and succumbed almost instantly. And so we leave the little snitch right smack up behind the eight-ball, and a good end for the mealy-mouthed, psalm-singing petty thief, if you ask me.

A Farewell to Omsk

THE TERRIFYING RESULT

OF READING AN ENTIRE

GIFT SET OF DOSTOIEVSKY

IN ONE AFTERNOON

*L*ATE one afternoon in January 18—, passers-by in L. Street in the town of Omsk might have seen a curious sight. A young man of a somewhat flushed, feverish appearance was standing outside Pyotr Pyotrvitch's tobacco shop. This in itself was interesting, as Pyotr Pyotrvitch had no tobacco shop in L. Street. Even had he had one, there would have been a large gaping hole in the sidewalk in front of it due to a sewer excavation, so that only the top of the young man's head would be visible. Of itself there was nothing unusual in the spectacle of a young man standing up to his knees in water staring fixedly at the fresh loam piled up about him. What amused the passers-by was that anyone should want to go into Pyotr Pyotrvitch's shop, since it was common knowledge that Pyotr had died some years before of the bends and his shop had been converted into an abbatoir or worse. Indeed, there were those who maintained that the shop had never been there at all—was, in short, a sort of mirage such as is often seen by travelers in the desert. But there was such a look of idealism on the young man's face, of the kind which is so often to be observed nowadays in our Russian university students, that the irreverent titters and cries of "Ach, pfoo!" were quickly silenced. Finally the young man sighed deeply, cast a look of determination around him, and entered the shop.

"Good afternoon, Pyotr Pyotrvitch!" he said resolutely.

"Good afternoon, Afya Afyakievitch!" replied the shopkeeper warmly. He was the son of a former notary public attached to the household of Prince Grashkin and gave himself no few airs in consequence. Whilst speaking it was his habit to extract a greasy barometer from his waistcoat and consult it importantly, a trick he had learned from the Prince's barber. On seeing Afya Afyakievitch he skipped about nimbly, dusted off the counter, gave one of his numerous offspring a box on the ear, drank a cup of tea, and on the whole behaved like a man of the world who has affairs of moment occupying him.

"Well, Afya Afyakievitch," he said with a sly smile, "what can I sell you today? Cigarettes, perhaps?"

"Cigarettes?" repeated the young man vaguely. A peculiar shudder passed over his frame as he regarded the

[94]

top of Pyotr's head intently. It was just wide enough to fit the blade of an ax. A strange smile played about his lips, and only the entrance of another personage distracted him. This was none other than Alaunia Alaunovna, the shopkeeper's daughter, a prostitute with a look of exaltation on her timid face, who entered and stood unobtrusively in a corner.

"How patient she is!" thought the young man, his heart touched. An overpowering desire to throw himself at her feet and kiss the hem of her garment filled his being.

"Well, well!" exclaimed Pyotr Pyotrvitch, anxious to impress his customer. "Allow me, kind sir, to present my daughter, Alaunia Alaunovna. She is a girl of education—he, he!" A stifling feeling overcame the young man; he wanted to throw himself at the man's feet and bite them. Alaunia Alaunovna dropped a small curtsy. The young man, a pitying expression on his face, picked it up and quickly returned it to her. She gave him a grateful glance named Joe.

"And—and what does your daughter do?" Afya asked with emotion.

"She is a prostitute in a small way of business," replied Pyotr proudly.

"It's great work if you can get it," the young man stammered.

"Permit me, it is the only way to live!" cried the shop-keeper excitedly. But by now Afya was even more excited than he was.

"Ah yes—excuse me—that is to say!" he began confusedly. A swarm of thoughts filled his brain. "I used to know a man, a titular councilor, Andron Andronovitch Pojarsky, in the province of Z——. We were in the Gymnasium together. Well, only fancy, last night I met him at the Petrovsky Bridge, as I was returning from Dunya's where we were having a discussion of certain ideas, I won't go into them, but Pimentov—he is a good-hearted fellow, he had entered into a free marriage with his cousin—tfoo, how I wander! Well, this Andron Andronovitch, poor fellow, is in a bad way, in a word is reduced to eating his rubbers, all he has left, in a certain sense. Ach, these Slavophiles!" broke off Afya, taking out some old pieces of cucumber and fish he had been carrying in his pocket and dipping them in his tea. "Just imagine, he has such extreme notions—Utopias, one might say. . . ."

"Yes! Yes!" interrupted Pyotr, nodding with great rapidity, almost perspiring with excitement. "But you spoke formerly of cigarettes, did you not? Here is a good brand—fifteen kopecks a package, or two packages for twenty-five kopecks. A brand much favored by the garrison, young gentleman!"

"Fifteen kopecks?" asked Afya slowly. "Then the second package must be only ten kopecks?"

"True, young sir," said Pyotr, screwing up his little red-rimmed eyes in the manner of one who is about to inspect a private aquarium. "But unfortunately I have only one package."

"Pyotr Pyotrvitch," said the young man quietly, "do you know what I think? I think this is a hell of a tobacco shop, in any language."

"You're telling *me?*" inquired Pyotr sadly. "Hey, where are you going? Just a moment—come, a cup of tea—let's have a discussion. . . ."

"I'll be right outside in that sewer excavation if you want me," said Afya over his shoulder. "I'd sort of like to brood over things for a while."

"Well, skip the gutter," sighed Pyotr.

"Don't take any flannel kopecks," said Afya gloomily. He dislodged a piece of cucumber from his tie, shied it at a passing Nihilist, and slid forward into the fresh loam.

Entered as Second-Class Matter

*W*HAT has gone before: Poultney Groin, disillusioned and middle-aged playboy, member of Manhattan's "upper crust," tires of Simone Dravnik, beauteous model whom he has been protecting. Womanlike, stung to the quick, she stares into her hand-mirror in her lavishly appointed apartment on Park Avenue and asks herself the age-old question: FINISHED YOUR DINNER? NOW IT'S ACID'S TURN TO DINE! THESE SMALL CAVITIES FILLED WITH DECOMPOSED FOOD MORSELS RAPIDLY HATCH BACTERIA. IN A FEW HOURS YOUR FORMERLY HEALTHY SYSTEM IS A MASS OF PUTREFACTION. ASK DR. FRITZ P. TANZPALAST OF THE UMBESCHRIEN HOSPITAL IN MUNICH. OR ASK MR. FRED DAHLGREN OF NORFOLK, VIRGINIA. DOG MAH CATS, FOLKS, JES' GIVE ME

MAH SPOON VITTLES, MAH SIDE-MEAT AN'
YAMS, AN' DAT LITTLE BLUE TIN OF EDGE-
WORTH, SHO SHO. Down the dusty Chisholm trail
into Abilene rode taciturn Spit Weaver, his lean brown
face an enigma and his six-gun swinging idly from the
pommel of Moisshe, the wonder horse. I'm curryin' my
dogs in a pail of hot H_2O when the ball-and-chain ankles
in beamin'. I get the bulge on her both ways from the
whistle. Listen, sister, I snarls, Spike McGinnity'll be a
pushover for the Kid's meathooks. He'll be kissin' the
canvas in two frames. So take a powder. You're slug-
nutty, grates she, how you gonna do it? Just bend the old
auditory apparatus, meanin' ear, I warbles. WOMEN
OF AMERICA, ALL YOU WORRIED FATTIES,
SIMPLY APPLY MY MARVELOUS THINNO
TREATMENT TO THOSE SAGGING, FOOLISH
BUBBIES OF YOURS AND IN TEN MINUTES
YOU'LL BE AS SVELTE AS A FIFTH AVENUE
MODEL—SVELTER, BY CHRIST. VY SVELTER
IN THE CITY'S HEAT WHEN POISED, SELF-
POSSESSED COSMOPOLITANS RUB ELBOWS
IN THE SALON MIXTE OF THE *NORMANDIE?*
MINGLE WITH COURTLY DIPLOMATS, SCIN-
TILLATING STARS OF STAGE AND SCREEN,
AND WORLD-FAMOUS BON VIVANTS IN THE
SPACIOUS, AIRY PLAYROOMS OF THIS FLOAT-

ING WEEK-END! SHOOT CLAY DUCKS IN THE PRIVACY OF YOUR CABIN! ROACH-RIDDEN, POCKMARKED, HOG-FAT, LAND-POOR, NIGGER-RICH, PENNY-WISE AND POUND-FOOLISH GENUINE BRETON STEWARDS ATTEND TO YOUR EVERY WANT! Beginning next month: Edith Waterhouse Prattfogle's dynamic novel of human destinies against the brilliant background of a Hawaiian volcano. A tapestry shot through and through with the vivid plumage of pleasure-mad sybarites. A flaming pageant of a forbidden love. White man . . . brown girl . . . caught in the volcanic drama of life . . . on the sun-drenched shores of a magic isle . . . where blood runs hot and the heart is free and man holds in fierce embrace the alluring image of elemental woman as the jealous God in the Mountain of Fire sunders the earth and splits the skies and hurls the sea to a bottomless pit because she broke the savage Taboo! SHAPE YOUR NOSE THE NEW SCIENTIFIC WAY WITH THIS NEW DEVICE DISCOVERED BY LEADING EUROPEAN CHEMISTS. FRECKLES, PIMPLES, WRINKLES, BLACKHEADS, ENLARGED PORES, PITS, POTS, PANS, ABRASIONS, PAINTER'S COLIC, TRACHOMA, TREACHERY, AND TRAINMAN'S HEADACHE ALL DISAPPEAR BEFORE THIS INVIGORATING COMPOUND. Dog of a Christian unbeliever, know then that in all Samarkand dwells none as lovely as gazelle-eyed Vashtar. Even the lotus petal fades before her modest demeanor, and when she walks abroad veiled in her yashmak, foolhardy indeed is he who would dare gainsay her. But in the crooked Street of Ten Thousand Lanterns wily Ah Gow fingered a jade-encrusted fly worth a prince's ransom and kept his own counsel. Verily is it written that the fool has a hundred tongues but the wise man will mother a clucking hen with soft speeches. Parsley Braddon of the violet eyes and the storm-tossed curls lounged moodily in her chaise-longue atop Gotham's loftiest skyscraper. Her exquisitely modeled shoulders shivered disgustedly at the thought of Southampton in August. *Feh! Ptoo!* If only Roddy Lathrop and Mimi Lubliner would call for her in their yellow speedster. To feel the giddy onrush of wind in her hair as she sped down the Merrick Road—free, free! LOTS O' FOLKS FIGGER THEY'RE SASSIETY FELLERS BECUZ THEY OWN A CLAW-HAMMER COAT. PUSSONALLY, I'D BE A DERN SIGHT HAPPIER A-WHITTLIN' CHAWS OFF'N MY OLD PLUG O' MECHANICS DELIGHT. AND MR. BURNS, HOWEVER HOMELY HIS PHILOSOPHY, IS RIGHT. THIS LITTLE BOX OF TASTY CHOC-OLATE CANDY . . . COLLAPSIBLE, EASILY CLEANED, FITS INTO ANY ORIFICE . . . WILL

BLOW THE BEJESUS OUT OF YOUR LAZY COLON. CLEAN HOUSE! CLEAR THE DECKS! CLEAR THE COURTROOM! OPEN YOUR BOWEL AND LET THE SUNLIGHT IN! It was glamour that put highlights in her hair, glamour that made him throw back his shoulders like a young Lochinvar come riding out of the West. Young they were, absurdly young . . . brave, defiant of the world, lazing the days away. All both of them wanted was a little nook. Foolish, tender, quixotic, impulsive, generous to a fault, they called me Aunt Vi, albeit I was scarcely three years their senior. At times their innocence and gay bravado brought a lump to my throat. TAKE THE LUMP OF MARGARINE, WHIP WELL WITH A SKEIN OF GRAY WORSTED, ROLL WELL IN BREADCRUMBS TILL YOUR SKIN GETS THAT TINGLY FEELING, AND THEN ASK THESE SIX QUESTIONS OF YOUR CHURCH TOILET SEAT. MY HUSBAND WAS TOUCHY, MOROSE, FLATULENT. HE WOULD LEAVE FOR HIS OFFICE IN THE MORNING, THROW HIMSELF AT HIS TYPEWRITER, AND PRACTICALLY TEAR THE CLOTHES OFF HER. I CONSULTED A SPECIALIST AND TOGETHER WE EXAMINED THE FINE, SAW-TOOTHED EDGES OF THE TISSUE UNDER THE MICROSCOPE. SURE ENOUGH . . .

[105]

THEY WERE SNAILS. WE HESITATED AT FIRST BUT AFTER THE GARÇON ASSURED US, WE TRIED THEM AND FOUND THEM DELICIOUS. WE ALSO VISITED LA REINE PEDAUQUE, WEBER'S, THE TOMB OF NAPOLEON, THE HOUSE OF ALL NATIONS, AND MANY OTHER SPOTS OF THE CITY OF LIGHT. ALL IN ALL THE TRIP COST US TWO HUNDRED AND FIVE DOLLARS, INCLUDING TIPS. WELL, DEAR BETTY, "NUF SED" FOR TONIGHT AND I CERTAINLY MUST SAY THAT THE FURNESS-WITHY LINES ARE ALL A BODY COULD WANT IN THE WAY OF ECONOMICAL, PLEASANT TRAVEL. OH, YES, AND I MUSTN'T NEGLECT TO TELL YOU THAT TWO SEVENTEEN-THOUSAND-TON, STEAM-HEATED LINERS LEAVE EVERY TUESDAY AND SATURDAY FOR HAIFA AND SMYRNA FROM PIER 89. To Tracy Hand, a formal figure with elegant hands erect by the rosewood spinet, his cravat a white patch of arrogance below his dark, alien face, the futility of life in Salem was a fact, a proved quantity. Poppaea couldn't, he knew, feel the resentment, inevitably, which he had been storing up inside him. The notes died in the twilight and he turned carefully, almost stiffly, toward the gun-room. However brittle his role in the succession of frivolities which he tolerated in this house, the memory of Lily Jastrow's laughter followed him. FRANKLY, WE'RE KNOX-LABEL-CON-SCIOUS . . . AND WHY NOT? WE'D BE DULL YOUNG MODERNS NOT TO REALIZE THAT *APRÉS TOUT* KNOX GELATIN HAS THAT CER-TAIN *JE NE SAIS QUOI* . . . THAT HOW YOU SAY *ÉLAN* . . . THAT MYSTERIOUS "SPREAD-ABLE" QUALITY POSSESSED ONLY BY THIS ZESTY OLD CHEDDAR DUSTED LIGHTLY OVER WHEATY LITTLE THINSIES. YOU THERE, UNCLE MOSE, YOU BLACK RASCAL, WHUFFO' AIN'T YOU DONE BRING IN DE CUNN'L'S FATBACK 'N' CO'N-PONE? FAIX AN' BEGORRA, AH'S BEEN SAVORING DE DE-LICIOUS ODOR OB CHASE AND SANBORN'S DATE-MARKED COFFEE, BEFO' DE LAWD! WELL, MOSE, I CERTAINLY CAN'T BLAME YOU FOR THAT, BUT WHERE DID YOU GET IT? WHY, BASCOM'S, JUST ABOVE FORTY-FOURTH STREET, YOU KNOW. Which explains how Mr. Demosthenes P. Johnson, late Grand Sachem of the Affiliated Sons of the Imperial Order of the Set-ting Star, happened to be walking down F Street in the Ethiopian quarter of Birmingham, Alabama. He had just passed the tonsorial parlors of T. Agamemnon Snowball

(Motto: We shave you, you save yourself) when he was hailed by a familiar voice. Turning, he descried the beaming lineaments of none other than Pericles Q. Shoat, late vice-president in charge of production of the Abyssinian Motion-Picture Studios. YOU AMERICAN MOTHERS, IN THOSE INTIMATE LITTLE HEART-TO-HEART TALKS WITH YOUR DAUGHTERS, WHAT ABOUT THIS QUESTION OF SHASHLIK (THE MEDICAL NAME FOR SOILED STOMACH)? YOU LIKE TO THINK OF YOURSELF AS A SISTER TO MARY ELLEN, NOT AS A MOTHER. AND YET YOU ARE ALLOWING THE FLUFF TO ACCUMULATE IN HER NAVEL AND STORE UP ILLNESSES FOR LATER YEARS. YOU MUST BE A PRETTY FLEA-BITTEN SON-OF-A-BITCH, DASH IT ALL! BUT THAT'S ONLY PART OF OUR SERVICE! WE, THE MAKERS OF ROYLCORD-BOUNCEAWAY TIRES, THE TIRE HABIT OF A NATION, THE TIRE WITH THE TRIPLE SUCTION GRIPS, THE DOUBLE REINFORCED SHOCK-ABSORBING CUSHION-IMPACT, AND THAT MODERN INNOVATION IN TIRE-ENGINEERING, FLOATING SHOULDER PRESSURE, HAVE POSTED A BOND WITH 184 OF AMERICA'S LEADING INSURANCE COMPANIES. IF ANY TIRE BEARING OUR

NAME BLOWS OUT IN LESS THAN SIX HUN-
DRED THOUSAND MILES OF USE, YOU CAN
TAKE IT AND SHOVE IT INTO THE NEAREST
POST-OFFICE AND RECEIVE POSTPAID AN
ABSOLUTELY NEW ONE IN EXCHANGE! RE-
MEMBER IT'S *SHISH KEBAB* (YOUR DOCTOR'S
NAME FOR SENSITIVE EPIDERMIC TISSUE)
WHICH SHORTENS YOUR SHAVE-LIFE! BOY,
YOU HAVEN'T FELT SHAVE-EASE ON YOUR
OLD SHAVE-SURFACE TILL YOU'VE DISCOV-
ERED SHAV-KOMFY, THE SHAVE-SECRET OF
THE AZTECS! Evening was a bright lasso drawing the
sun's red ball behind the ridge when Virgil Spafford
stopped the Ford outside Gedney's. Man-fashion, he
made as if to pass April, laughing there in the little circle
of onhangers. She was a bright lasso drawing awkward
young men down from the farms. Virgil snorted; her
hand fluttered from his coat, and he entered Gedney's.
Gedney's, the bright lasso which drew the main street of
Shoreham into a hard, angular knot, was empty, partially
through having burned down the previous month, partially because old man Gedney had never set foot in
Shoreham. BRAZILIAN PEONS, HUMMING THEIR
NATIVE SONGS, PICKED THE COFFEE WHICH
FLAVORS THIS NEW AND STARTLING CON-
FECTION; FROM THE SNOWY SUMMITS OF

THE ANDES CAME LONG-FIBRED LLAMA WOOLS TO GIVE IT BODY; AND FROM OUR OWN PENNSYLVANIA COAL-FIELDS COMES THE DELICIOUS GRITTY ANTHRACITE DUST WHICH IS MAKING THIS OBSCENE LITTLE CANDY THE LUNCH-SUBSTITUTE OF MILLIONS. A mischievous breeze molded the outline of her figure against the dunes. Cap'n Eben Mushmouth chuckled to himself and relit his pipe. Sairy Ann would have plenty to say about this new arrival in Hyannis. FORTY FATHOM MACKEREL, SCALES GLISTENING WITH THE STILL-FRESH BRINE OF THE GEORGES BANK, BURSTING WITH IMPATIENCE TO LEAP INTO YOUR FRYING-PAN AND TREAT YOUR PALATE TO A REAL OLD-FASHIONED TUMMY-FEST! IN GALVANIZED-IRON HERMETICALLY SEALED PAILS DIRECT FROM OUR CLEANING SHEDS IN GLOUCESTER TO YOUR DOORSTEP! And now, dear reader, a final word from Mr. Editor Mans. We have scoured the fiction market to set before you THREE MILLION TINY SWEAT GLANDS FUNCTIONING in that vibrant panorama of tomorrow so that YOUR SENSITIVE BOWEL MUSCLES CAN react to the inevitable realization that only by enrichment and guidance PLUS A SOOTHING DEPILATORY can America face

ENTERED AS SECOND-CLASS MATTER
its problems confidently, unafraid, WELL-GROOMED,
MOUTH-HAPPY, BREAKING THE HAIR OFF AT
THE ROOTS WITHOUT UNDUE STENCH.
OKAY, MISS AMERICA!

Annual Navigation Report

SWARMS of letters have been settling like bees the last ten days on our Navigation, Coastwise and Pound-Foolish Department, whimpering plaintively for spring shipping news. People whose faces paled formerly at a salt breeze have been going around calking seams, laying keels, and battening down hatches with gusto, procured at the corner grocery store. The National Retail Informal Greengrocers' Association reports that unless foreign gusto imports increase, there will be a schism in the ranks of domestic gusto growers ending in a general massacre of all Huguenots over the age of twelve. Even in the ranks of the "Four Hundred" shipping fever has raised its ugly head; any morning one can see a knot of débutantes at Pierre's or the Park Lane toying with a bit of oakum in between the caviar and the roast mongoose. No less a personage than Mrs. Dolores del Schultz was glimpsed at a bazaar wearing a broadtail wrap trimmed with riding lights and caught up at the throat with a belaying-pin.

The most impressive change in the transatlantic liners this season was wrought in the *Queen Mary*, which installed a glass bottom so that passengers could look at marine life. Unfortunately, on the eastbound trip to Cherbourg the under side of the glass was clotted with flying sponges, which had never seen anything like the passengers on the *Queen Mary*. When questioned as to their reactions, the sponges confessed to a feeling of nausea and went home scuffing their feet. No other signs of sea life appeared during the next four days, and several of the passengers went to the purser in a body to complain. The latter pointed out that the *Queen Mary* was still tied up to the wharf and that it was a little early to expect anything. He thought, however, that they ought to see some water in a few days.

The *Normandie*, its face suffused with blushes at being outdone by the Limies, installed a glass bottom also, so that the first-class nabobs could look down at the tourist and steerage passengers. Deck stewards, after some hesitation, then allowed the travelers to lower their lines, baited with bits of pork. Two rather vinegary school-teachers were immediately hauled in, but had to be thrown back, as they were too large around the waist to pass through the hoop as required by the Bay of Fundy fishery rules. As all the pork was gone, the lines were baited with pieces of deck steward, this time with more success. A small shoal of vealy college boys, plump and juicy, was drawn in smiling toothily and was rushed off forthwith to the cook's galley to be made into a chowder. That evening the dining room was a blaze of lights and pulsating rhythm as obsequious waiters laid out the flawless knavery and polished the diamond-studded forks. But where was the chowder? Luxurious stage stars, social luminaries, and tight-lipped captains of finance raised their plucked eyebrows in surprise. Already impatient diners were beginning to beat on their plates with their spoons.

"This—this is infamous, sir!" spluttered one choleric old gentleman with walrus mustaches, twirling his red face angrily between his fingers. "Humph! Is this the service one hears about? Gad, sir, I shall go to the bottom of this!" The captain attempted to soothe him in vain. At last the chief mate arrived with troubled mien and whispered a few words into his superior's ear.

"Ladies and gentlemen," stammered the captain, "I regret to inform you that the cook has been eaten by the chowder." A great moan of pity and fear went up. Suddenly a man sprang to his feet.

"Are we slaves, men?" he demanded. "Must we starve

lumpishly till the end comes? Are we then at the mercy of these wolves in sheep's forms?"

"No, no!" shouted the diners. "You mean . . . ?"

"To the boats!" cried their self-appointed leader, quickly distributing sabres, muskets, and dirks. In a flash the dining room was emptied and they were on the boats. The death-cries of the boats, caught off their guard, filled the air. Carnage was everywhere. A moment later dainty women were rolling up the sleeves of their evening gowns to scrape the scales off the boats and take out the bones. A smell of delicious fried boats was pervading the ship, and many a fastidious dowager sniffed appreciatively as she balanced her peas on her nose and prepared to eat.

Three hours later they were sighted by a lonely Gloucesterman brawling for mackerel off the Georges Bank. The passengers crowded to the rail joyfully, and the house flag fluttered to the peak as the band broke into "Pony Boy, Pony Boy." And as Editha and Jessie sank sleepily into the warm blankets and hot coffee which the crew of the Mary Briscoe had provided, both agreed that it had been a simply thrilling day. Adventure, shipwreck, and mutiny—what more could any healthy girl want? Editha chuckled as she thought of the gasp of wonderment she would wring from her schoolfellows when she recounted her adventures. It had certainly been a red-letter day for "The Girls of Neat's-foot Hall."

The Love Decoy

A STORY OF YOUTH IN

COLLEGE TODAY—AWAKE,

FEARLESS, UNASHAMED

ROFESSOR GOMPERS is ill!"

The whisper spread like wildfire through the packed classroom. A feeling of emulsion swept over me. Kindly old Professor Gompers, whose grizzled chin and chiselled grin had made his name a byword at Tunafish College for Women! Ivy Weiskopf, sauciest co-ed in the class, she of the unruly locks and the candied gray eyes, leaned over to impart the latest gossip.

"That new instructor, Russell Gipf, is subbing for him!" The color drained slowly from my face, entered the auricle, shot up the escalator, and issued from the ladies' and misses' section into the kitchenware department. I remembered Russell Gipf as a lean brown giant in tweeds whose resemblance to Warren William had caused his suspension the year before. It had been an ugly scandal but luckily his nose was broken in an auto accident soon after and the faculty had restored him. Dreamily I recalled an autumn afternoon when I had visited him in his office in ivy-covered Schneider to discuss a theme I had written. Through the half-open windows drifted the mingled smell of wood smoke and freshmen. He confided that he was doing research in dirty limericks for his doctor's thesis and asked if I knew any "Good Ones." In the twinkling of an eye we were in the gutter. At no time, however, did he allow himself the usual indecent proposal, and I returned to my dormitory room raging, determined never to see him again.

An impatient voice summoned me rudely from my daydream. I looked up; Russell Gipf was addressing me crisply from the platform. My feminine eye noted that he was still a spiffy dresser, a regular up-to-the-minute gink.

"Will you please answer the question, Miss Hornbostel?"

"I—I didn't hear it," I quavered. Deep in my heart I hated him for lousing up my revery.

"Well, Miss Sly Boots," he retorted sardonically, "maybe you had better stop galvanizing around nights and pay attention!" A cold fury welled up in me and I longed to hang one on his lug for his insolence. I was seething but he could not see it, for several of my girl chums were seething in front of me. A moment later the bell tolling in ivy-covered Hoffenstein brought the class to a close. Slipping my pencil box and pen wipers into my corsage I approached his desk, a plan fermenting in my brain.

"Yes, Miss Hornbostel?" Russell Gipf's eyes were dancing with fun.

"Oh, Mr. Gipf," I began, "I hardly know how to say this. It—it's so personal." His eyes stopped dancing with fun and began dancing with sex.

"Go on," he urged.

"I—I can't get the cap off my toothpaste," I faltered, a tear trembling on my nose. "If you could only help me . . ." I gazed out of my huge bedroom eyes appealingly.

"Well, now—ahem—this is serious," he said slowly. "No wonder you weren't prepared in class just now. Naturally, you were upset."

"And you were cruel," I said.

"I'm sorry," he added Quigley.

"Why did you add Quigley?" I begged him. He apologized and subtracted Quigley, then divided Hogan. We hastily dipped the slices of Hogan into Karo, poured sugar over them, and ate them with relish.

"Tell me," said Gipf, as he wiped his mouth on the tail of his shirt, "about this toothpaste: if you could bring the tube to my office . . ."

I explained hurriedly that it was too heavy to carry and that he would have to come up to my dormitory room that evening after "lights out." He readily fell in with my wish and promised. As we walked across the campus toward ivy-covered Lapeedis, I drew him out craftily. He had been in the north of Scotland that summer shooting bob-tail flushes, and he was full of his subject. Although I hated him, I had to confess that his smile made my pulses 'sing, and I gladly would have leaped through a hoop had he asked me to. He must have been aware of it, for he suddenly reached into his green baize bag and produced a hoop.

"Here, leap through this hoop, you," he ordered. I did so and he flicked me lightly with his whip. I saw his face go dark with passion. "Dolores—I love you!" he whispered, his hand closing over mine. Mine in turn closed over his. In an instant we had chosen up sides, it was my turn at bats, and I knocked a sizzling bunt to Pipgrass in the daisies.

"Ah, cara mia, giz a kiz," panted Russell. I tried to resist his overtures but he plied me with symphonies, quartets, chamber music and cantatas. I felt myself softening, but I was determined to go through with my plan.

"Are you mad, Russell?" I stopped him haughtily. He bit his lip in a manner which immediately awakened my maternal sympathy, and I helped him bite it. Foolish man! In a trice the animal in him rose to the surface again. He caught my arm in a vise-like grip and drew me to him, but with a blow I sent him groveling. In ten minutes he was back with a basket of appetizing fresh-picked grovels. We squeezed them and drank the piquant juice thirstily. Then I blew him an airy kiss.

"Tonight—at ten-thirty, *mon désir!*" I flung at him over my shoulder. Even in my room I could hear him panting four floors below on the campus as I changed to a filmy negligee and began to cold-cream my glowing cheeks.

The dim glow of shaded lamps and the heady intoxication of incense had transformed my room into a veritable Oriental bower when Russell Gipf knocked cautiously on my door at ten-thirty. From my chaise-longue where I was stretched out lazily fingering a trashy French novel I murmured an inviting "Come in!"

"Come in!" I murmured invitingly. He entered swiftly, shaking himself vigorously. There had been a heavy fall of talcum several hours before and as far as the ground could see the eye was white. I offered Russell a dish of soap flakes, but despite my attempts to put him at his ease he seemed nervous.

"The—the toothpaste," he began, looking about suspiciously. I indicated the bathroom with a lazy finger. In a moment he reappeared, his face haggard and his eyes like burning holes in the snow.

"Yes," I shot at him coldly, "I tricked you. No, it's useless to try the door—and it's a four-story drop straight down from those windows, Mr. Russell Gipf. Perhaps you're wondering what I intend to do now." I picked up the telephone, my voice a snarl. "In five minutes the faculty will break in and find you in a co-ed's room. What will your wealthy old father Prosper Gipf, president of the Drovers and Plovers National Bank, say to that?" He backed away from me whimpering piteously. But I was goading him on as only a raging woman can. "You humiliated me in front of all my classmates today. Now—you shall pay." My hand was lifting the receiver when a faint scratching sounded at the door, followed by stertorous breathing. I threw it open. Dean Fothergill, his face that of a man mad with desire, lunged at me.

"Dolores," he implored, "you adorable little witch—I've been following you with my eyes—I . . ."

"You rotter!" I turned in surprise at Russell Gipf's voice as he flashed past me and drove a decisive blow into the aged roué's kidneys. The two men grappled, their teeth bared. Russell's head snapped back as Dean Fothergill, who I forgot to say was once amateur light-heavyweight boxing champion of University of Southern California at Los Angeles, drove a decisive blow to the Gipf kidneys. The noise of fist on kidneys rang out in the still air. I watched the spectacle unmoved. After all, tomorrow I would have to pass my law exam; I opened *Fist on Kidneys* and was deep in it when I heard a groan. I looked up. There, manacled to Russell Gipf, stood Dean Fothergill, a hangdog expression on his face.

"Well, Miss Hornbostel," he admitted shamefacedly, "I guess the jig is up."

"Tell her, you swine!" grunted Russell menacingly, pounding his windward kidney.

"I—I am Jim the Penman," said Fothergill with bowed head. "I forged the notes which sent your father, Harry Trefusis, to the cooler."

"Then you are Renssalaer Van Astorbilt, Russell?" I queried, dazed. He put his strong young arms about me and nodded shyly.

"Now may I ask you that question?" he blushed.

"Yes, Donald," I told him, hiding my scarlet face in his shoulder. Outside, the insupportable sweetness of a guitar cleft the warm summer air and bewhiskered, beflanneled, bewitched, bewildered, bejasused and bejabered undergraduates strolled under the hoary elms. And to this day, as I lie in my bed with the wind howling outside, I ofttimes seem to hear the hoarse croak of Long John Silver's parrot calling "Pieces of eight! Pieces of eight!" and the tapping of the blind man's stick outside the Admiral Benbow Inn.

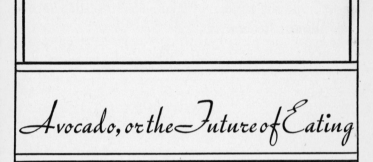

Avocado, or the Future of Eating

(NOTE FOUND IN AN EMPTY
STOMACH OFF SANTA
BARBARA)

*O*NE day not long ago in Los Angeles I found myself, banderillas in hand, facing the horns of a dilemma. I had gone into a Corn Exchange bank to exchange some corn and had fallen into conversation with the manager. He was very affable and insisted I inspect the assets of the branch, which included, among other things, the teeth Bryant Washburn had used in his film career. Issuing into the hot sunlight of the street, I was dismayed to find that it was time for lunch, and since I had forgotten to bring along a bag of pemmican, I would have to eat in Los Angeles—a fairly exact definition of the term "the kiss of death." I looked around me. On my left I could obtain a nutburger (hamburger with chopped walnuts, double ball of vanilla on the side) and a Giant Malted Milk Too Thick For a Straw; on my right the feature was barbecued pork fritters and orangeade. Unnerved, I stopped a passing street Arab and courteously inquired where I might find a cheap but clean eating house. Phil the Fiddler (for it was he) directed my steps to a pharmacy bearing the legend "Best Drug Stores, Inc." Merely for the record, I dined off an avocado sandwich on whole wheat and a lime rickey, and flunked my basal-metabolism test later that afternoon. I don't pretend to blame the management for my physical shortcomings; all I want them to do is laugh off their menu, a copy of which I seem to have before me.

In general, "Soda Fountain Suggestions" (Best Drug Stores, Inc.) is an attractively printed job in two colors (three if you count the gravy), and though it can hardly hope to rival the success of Gone with the Wind, I suppose there is an audience which will welcome it. The salads and three-decker sandwiches are treated with a certain gaiety and quaint charm which recall Alice of Old Vincennes. The banana splits and hot-and-cold Ovaltines are handled with a glib humor in the text, which is more than I can say for the way they are handled behind the fountain. The day I was there, a simply appalling oath escaped the lips of one of the dispensers when he dropped some fudge on his shoe. The authors have included a very disarming foreword short enough to quote in its entirety: "It is our earnest desire to fulfill the name that we have chosen for our chain, THE BEST. We can only

AVOCADO

accomplish this by serving you best. Any criticisms or suggestions will be appreciated by the management." Only a churl would decline so graceful a gambit. *Messieurs, en garde!*

Specifically, gentlemen of the management, my criticism concerns that cocky little summary of yours at the bottom of the menu. "BEST Soda Fountains," you proclaim flatly, "are BEST because: the ice creams contain no 'fillers' (starch, albumen, etc.); the syrups are made from cane sugar and real fruits; the coffee is a special blend made the modern Silex way with a specially filtered water," and so forth. Lest some of the younger boys in the troop think the millennium has come to the City of Our Lady, Queen of the Angels, what are the facts?

In the first place, you needn't think you can woo me with any such tinsel as "the ice creams contain no 'fillers' (starch, albumen, etc.)." One thing I'll have in my ice cream or it's no dice—and that's fillers. I don't even insist on ice cream as long as I can stuff myself with fillers. You heap my plate with albumen and starch (any kind, even laundry starch) and stand clear. Call me a piggy if you want to, but I just can't get *enough* of that starch.

Quite honestly, your statement that the syrups "are made from cane sugar and real fruits" surprised me. If that's a boast, I must say it's a pretty hollow one. It might interest you to know that back in 1917 the Allied High

[133]

Command specified *beet* sugar and *false* fruits in all syrups purchased by its commissary departments. Didn't know that, did you? Probably too busy evading the draft at the time. Well, you just ask any biochemist his recommendation on sugars, as I did recently; you'll get the same terse answer: beet sugar and false fruits. I have this cousin of mine who is a perfect wiz at chemistry—really astonishing marks for a boy of nineteen in high school—and no matter what you ask him, he'll give you the same answer: beet sugar and false fruits. Frankly, the family's getting a little worried about it; they have to keep Benny chained to a ring in the floor most of the time.

Furthermore, it's useless to try to creep into my heart with any blandishments like "the coffee is a special blend made the modern Silex way with a specially filtered water." Filtering Los Angeles water robs it of its many nourishing ingredients, not the least of which is chow mein. It is an interesting fact, known to anybody who has ever been interned in that city or its suburbs, that the water possesses a rich content of subgum almond chow mein, Cantonese style, and one or two cases have even been reported where traces of peanut candy and lichee nuts were found. The assertion of a friend of mine that he once saw a Filipino houseboy come out of a water faucet, of course, must be regarded as apocryphal. The Filipinos are a wiry little people, but they are not as wiry as all that. Nor are they ready as yet for the self-government which my distinguished opponents, the gentlemen of the affirmative, claim they should have. And so, honorable judges and ladies and gentlemen, we of the negative conclude that the Filipinos should not be given their independence because (1) we need them for a coaling station, (2) there is a high percentage of illiteracy, and (3) if we do, Japan will soon be snatching up Guam—or "chewing Guam," so to speak. I thank you.

Footnote on the Yellow Peril

*I*F YOU have been bothered with any mysterious aches or pains this summer, Bellevue Hospital has been going around the last few days cockily puffing out its chest because it has acquired a new laboratory of tropical medicine. Just drop down there and they will be glad to tell you at a glance whether you are suffering from sprue, the Delhi boil, Madura foot, Bilharzia and related fluke diseases (Bilharzia is no fluke, let me tell you; there's nobody to blame but yourself), the Peruvian wart, or any of the various forms of pork trichinae. I am even thinking of going down there myself for a little reupholstering. Mine isn't exactly a physical thing, unless I caught something from reading Alice Tisdale Hobart's books; it's more of a Far Eastern mental complaint. I just can't seem to tell those Chinese war lords apart.

The trouble started some months ago when Chiang,

the Premier of China (have I made any mistakes so far?), went over to borrow a cup of opium from Chang and exchange gossip. Now, that shouldn't be hard: Chiang went to chin with Chang. This Chang is "Young" Chang and should not be confused with "Old" Chang, his father, the one-time ruler of Manchuria. As soon as I found this out, I started confusing them, and it didn't help any to learn that "Young" Chang has two brothers of the same name. One of them is this harum-scarum younger brother whom the Chinese simply adore and call "that murtherin' shpalpeen, wurra wurra." The other is a Communist and lives in Moscow; his people distinguish him from his brother as "Faith, that murtherin' Rooshian bhoyo."

Just when I had all this neatly pegged and was going along leading a life of Buddhistic calm, contemplating my navel, Chang decided to kidnap Chiang. What his motive was I can't imagine, unless it was to confuse me horribly. The paper I read it in unfortunately happened to carry as well a publicity release about a new book called "Yang and Yin." At the close of business that day, the old prickly sensation had returned and I found myself bursting into tears over the most trivial matters. I spent a white night trying to straighten myself out, but by morning all I managed to remember was that I had once seen a film called "Chang" with a very cute monkey in it. I had barely pinned on my pigtail and sat down to my breakfast of steamed rice and bamboo shoots when a woman representing herself as my wife lifted her head from a theatrical magazine and asked me if I had ever seen Della Fox in "Wang." I slid out of my chair barking like a Pekingese and mercifully fainted away.

It was touch and go with me for forty-eight hours, and I'd like to take this opportunity of thanking my wife and the three concubines for their unsparing devotion in my behalf. Soon, however, the crisis was past, and then came long, slow days of convalescence, with my collie bounding beside me on the lawn and tugging at my parasol. Good old Towser! I'd like to take this opportunity of thanking him for his unsparing devotion. For it was on Towser that the burden fell of dressing the children, undressing the concubines, and eating my gruel, without which I would have recovered in half the time.

As soon as my Number One boy spread word through the compound that the foreign devil was well again, the Chinese sprang to attention. "Young" Chang ("Old" Chang's son, but not "Scalawag" Chang or "Red" Chang) offered to return the Generalissimo (you'd better hold onto the rails; I'm beginning to pitch slightly) to Soong, who didn't give a hang but was only negotiating for his sister (who is married to Chiang). At this point two more generals, who had been waiting in the wings until they heard my pulses begin to hammer, entered the scene. Their names might just as easily have been Rosencrantz and Guildenstern, but no; they had to be named Yang and Feng. Yang was a Chinese version of General Jubal A. Early who hoped to highjack the whole enterprise; Feng, who is called "the Christian Marshal" (as opposed to Feng, the Jewish Marshal, I guess), had no real business there, but claimed the conductor had given him a wrong transfer. Chang—no, Yang—told Chiang—wait a minute, *Chiang* told Yang that Feng, who is Soong . . .

From now on everything is quicksand, and if it's all right with you, I'll just sit here under this banyan tree and read a nice, quiet book. I'm almost halfway through Jack London's *White Fang*, but it isn't holding me. I may slip around the corner to the movies—they have a very interesting picture there, I understand. It's called *The General Died at Dawn*, about a Chinese war lord named Yang. The only trouble is that Clifford Odets, who wrote it, has just married Luise Rainer, and she plays the lead in *The Good Earth*, which is about a character named Wang. And now they tell me Mr. Odets is going to do a story for a producer named Wanger. *For goodness' sake, has everybody gone stark, staring Wang?*

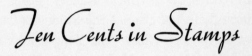

A LAYMAN'S EASY GUIDE

TO FLIRTING

*I*F *New Book of Flirtations*, No. 18, red-hot from the presses of Messrs. I. & M. Ottenheimer of Baltimore, doesn't stand New York society on its ear this winter, then I for one will gladly turn in my pledge pin. That buzzing sound you undoubtedly heard last Tuesday was the blood hammering in the pulses of Doubleday Doran, Simon & Schuster, and Mr. Viking. Already smart hostesses the country over have let back-gammon sets fall from listless fingers and have buried eager noses in this new dictionary of the voluptuous arts. Those of us who thought the Ottenheimer peak had been reached with *50 New Hash-House Jokes*, *25 Breezy Wop Dialect Jokes*, and *Revised Witches' Dream Book* woke up the other morning to find things popping. Personally I wouldn't give six bits for Mr. Knopf's whole nervous system when this book gets on the counters.

[145]

As a makeup job, *New Book of Flirtations, No.* 18 is nothing to let down your hair about. The title page of my copy has the subhead: "Containing the Language of Postage-Stamps, All the Secret Signs, Insinuations and Captivations, Also the Art of Flirting with Cane, Fan, Handkerchief, etc., Also Language of Flowers and Autograph-Album Verses." In short, a lot of Bodoni, and the smear of Tarvia in the lower left-hand corner didn't help much. It might be a hunch to omit that Tarvia touch from the second edition. It only confuses the reader.

Speaking as one who was drummed out of the Boy Scouts for flunking the Morse-code test, I found the handkerchief, fan, cane, postage-stamp, parasol, hat, glove, whip, cigar, and pencil flirtations nothing if not complicated. There are over two hundred things you can do with these little fetishes which mean something in the language of love. For instance, breaking a cigar in half. You and I probably break hundreds of cigars in half some days when we are going good and never even give it a second thought. Yet E. Phillips Ottenheimer, that old sleuth, has discovered that breaking a cigar in half means "I wish to speak to you." Imagine the result if Macy's scrapped its pushbutton system and installed cigar signals. This means that Mr. Ganz in Ladies' Frillies would have to break a hundred Bayuks an hour just to attract the attention of Julius, the stockroom boy. Not that a knowledge of cigar flirtations hasn't its advantages. One afternoon last month, while I was trying to get nickels out of a telephone booth in the Bronx, I noticed a rather fly-looking customer blowing smoke slowly downward from his cigar and ogling the pretty cigar-woman behind the counter. This was patently the signal "I love you," and the blush which suffused the young lady's alabaster throat confirmed it. The incident had a startling climax. The girl's father intercepted the signal, reddened with rage, and went into bankruptcy some four days later. The swain's mortification was comical in the extreme.

The parasol flirtations are even more involved. "Carrying elevated in left hand" means "I desire your acquaintance." I would desire the acquaintance of anybody, no matter how repulsive, whom I found "carrying elevated in left hand." Not even the Mayor's Traction Committee would attempt that without flinching. As for Dining-Table Signaling, the next time anybody balances a knife on a fork in your presence, you'd better keep your eyes peeled. In case you don't know it, he has just made a date to meet her at the gate after dinner, and unless you're not a "slow poke," Miss Muffet will "give you the gate for fair," as the saying goes.

But it is the whip flirtations in particular which make one's head reel. Holding the butt of a whip against your right eye, according to the omniscient Ottenheimers, is nothing more or less than "I am engaged." So that plunging the butt of the whip into the left eye must mean "You are, are you?" It is good to know that when Simon Legree coils the lash of his whip around the stock and starts toward Eva, what he really means is "May I have the next dance?" I should love to see *Uncle Tom's Cabin* again in the light of my new whip symbolism. Especially that delicate scene just before the second-act curtain when Legree roguishly taps the stock on his left forearm. Whoever would have thought that meant "Will you bathe with me?" And to think Mrs. Stowe came from such respectable people in Brooklyn.

But like everything else, it isn't long before the worm of Sex starts gnawing on the apple of Love; and on Page 37, Directions for Kissing are being bruited about. "Always breathe on her a warm breath when you kiss her, especially on the center of the forehead and the back of the neck; in caressing her always move your hands over her arms from her shoulders downward to the tips of her fingers." After this little circulation-getter, you are ready for the chaste salute on the lips. It is a long time since I simmered over *Mademoiselle de Maupin*, but if those Ottenheimer boys couldn't give Gautier cards and spades for torrid kiss data, I'll eat the page this comes from: "Her lips are almost open. Lean slightly forward with

your head, not your body; take good aim; the lips meet—
the eyes close—the heart opens—the soul rides the storm,
sorrows, and troubles of life—heaven opens before you—
the world shoots from under your feet as a meteor flies
across the evening sky—the nerves dance before the altar
of love as zephyrs dance with dew-trimmed flowers—the
heart forgets its bitterness, and the art of kissing is
learned. No noise, no fuss."

And they call us a nation of money-grubbers!

— II —

Hip-Hip-Hypnosis!

A glance through Freud—after the ladies have retired
to the arboretum and left you and the professor to your
port wine and cheroots—should be enough to tell you
that Love and Sleep are the handmaidens of the Muses.
"Look for one and you will inevitably find the other,"
said Heine. (And while you are looking, try to find *that*
quotation somewhere.) Well, both Love and Sleep got a
break with the publishers recently; and amateur hypnotists
are bolting their oatmeal these mornings and rushing out
to buy, borrow, beg, or steal a copy of Professor M.
Young's daring brochure, *25 Lessons in Hypnotism, being*

the Most Perfect, Complete, Easily Learned and Comprehensive COURSE in the World. Embracing the Science of Magnetic Healing, Telepathy, Mind Reading, Clairvoyant Hypnotism, Mesmerism, Animal Magnetism, Thought Transference, Personal Magnetism, and Kindred Sciences. Not since the mighty Mesmer retired from the platform has such a tohu-bohu been raised in applied hypnotics. By Tuesday we can safely expect advertisements in the morning papers reading: " 'Amazing, swiftly paced, chockful of the insight we have come to expect of Professor Young.'—Walter Yust in Philadelphia Ledger."

I couldn't help feeling from the first that the title of the book was a bit cumbersome. Something like Master Skylark would have been easier for Mr. Average Book-Lover to remember. Despite the length of the title, however, Professor Young is a man of few words, and he wastes none of them getting away from the barrier. He assures you at the outset that there is practically nobody or nothing you can't hypnotize if you only follow directions. Not only humans, but hens, sparrows, pigeons, rabbits, and crabs yield with equal ease to his will. Simply press down the head and draw a chalk line on the ground starting from the beak. My knowledge of crab life has been limited to throwing the occasional ones I encountered a cooky, but if those cunning crustaceans do have beaks, it doesn't mean they intend to let you draw chalk lines from them. Furthermore, the professor neglects to mention the purpose of such trickery. One would have to be a pretty horrid fellow indeed to get any pleasure out of having a pigeon or a crab in one's power. I am afraid Professor Young is more the dreamer type.

The technique of hypnotizing one's fellow-man is simplicity itself. A bright object, like a gold watch, held before the eyes, the word "sleep" repeated forcefully several times, and your subject is a harp to play on as you will. From this it is only a step to Page 21, where we find ourselves already "Extracting Teeth by Hypnotism." Here is the method, easily memorized if you are going to a party some evening where the occasion may arise: "Hypnotize someone who desires a tooth extracted. Make proper suggestions, such as 'You feel no pain. Your face and neck can feel nothing, absolutely nothing.' Have a dentist present and let him extract the tooth. When the subject awakens he will not know the tooth is out. He will suffer no pain whatever, either during or after the operation." If this bombshell doesn't set a new low in Novocaine common, nothing will. The only trouble is that such a display might easily turn the meeting into a dental orgy, with everybody toothless by midnight. Still, it might be one way for the hostess to save money on the refreshments if all else fails.

"How to Hypnotize a Bad Boy" is easily the high spot of the book, although "How to Hypnotize a Roomful of People at One Time" has its points. Once you have the bad boy under your spell, you begin with a little flattery: "You are a bright manly boy. You will never lie. No! No! You will never strike your sister again. You will never fight the other boys because sunshine is in your heart and sunshine is in your mind. My good boy, my bright boy, my happy boy." Your good, bright, and happy boy then awakes and inaugurates his redemption by plunging a Meccano girder into your right eye.

Fifty rather unique "entertainments" have been outlined in the latter part of his book by Professor Young for the amusement of young and old. "Tractable" is hardly the word to describe your subjects if you have done your preliminary work carefully. I quote at random:

"No. 10. Suddenly change your subjects into very old people. Have some deaf, others toothless, others lame, others blind. The transformation from youth to old age will be very funny."

"No. 29. Select a subject who talks easily under the influence. Hypnotize him and make the suggestion that when he awakens he will be the President of the United States, etc. Now awaken him and a few moments later a strange look will come into his eyes and he will commence a remarkable political speech. The power of even the most ignorant person to make a political speech under hypnotic influence is really most remarkable and baffles explanation."

"No. 44. Give him a glass with a few drops of water in it; tell him that it is a pint of peanuts and he will calmly pour them into his pocket."

And now that everyone in your audience has wiped the tears of laughter from his eyes, what about the patient who seems reluctant about awakening? "Should the subject experience a difficulty in opening his eyes, then with the tips of the thumbs the operator should rub briskly from the root of the nose outward toward the temples, and finish by blowing or fanning."

But if—but if he . . . Well, just call in the coroner.

— III —

Scratch a Penn and Find a Tartar

How to Get a Job Through Help Wanted Advertisements, by Jacob Penn, is a horse of a totally different feather. And a horse, incidentally, which will leap the highest employment hurdle if you know what to avoid in your letter of application. For instance: "I have found girls and women using the oddest, queerest forms of paper and envelopes imaginable. Some even inclosed 'three kisses' for the prospective employer, while others used rare perfumes to attract the attention without success." Time enough for the kisses later on, Miss Winsome Typist; and sowing rare perfumes will only net you a crop of dragon's teeth, worthless unless you are going into mechanical dentistry. Above all, warns M. Penn, don't try to whitewash your last dismissal. Just use one of the suggested formulas: "Dismissed for leaving my work and going to the ball game. But I have learned my lesson, and will know better in the future." Or "I was discharged because I was found playing cards in the paint shop. I got my medicine and I assure you I will never again be accused of this or any other bad behavior." Of course, you will have to adapt these for your own needs. If your last job was that of an orderly in the Ellin Speyer Hospital, your excuse would read: "I was discharged because I was found playing cards in the distemper ward (Lafayette Street side). I got distemper and I assure you I will never again be accused of this or any other bad behavior. I am at Stud, New Jersey, for the week-end and will be glad to grant you an interview."

One letter in particular, contained in the appendix under "Successful Model Letters," won me in a walk:

TEN CENTS IN STAMPS

Dear Sir:

For two summers I worked in the lace department of Hart & Hart, 45 Lexington Avenue, this city. I would have been with them now, after graduation, had they not gone into bankruptcy last month.

I am familiar with the lace business. I refer you to Mr. Harold A. Warner, who was in charge of the lace department when I worked there. Mr. Warner lives in Annadale. I also refer you to Mr. Robert Nash, 675 Tiber Street, who is competent to speak of my honesty, industry, and character, having known me since I was a baby.

I am 17 and expect a salary of $15.00 per week.

Respectfully yours,

Willard Herbert.

There was a downright frankness about Willard's letter which moved me, and I hope he will pardon me for replying with equal honesty:

Dear Mr. Herbert:

We have looked up your references and find that Mr. Warner absconded last Tuesday with the petty hart of Cash & Cash, the firm you claim you worked for. For your own records, Mr. Warner is not living in Annadale at present. His address is Box 1282, Ossining, New York. Mr. Robert Nash of 675 Tiber Street admits he has known you since you were a baby. All he can recall is that you were a particularly dirty feeder.

We note with interest that you have copied your letter from the appendix of Jacob Penn's *How to Get a Job Through Help Wanted Advertisements.* If you will call with a wheelbarrow Friday morning, we shall be glad to turn over to you at no cost fifty-four pounds of similar letters which I had to open. I hope the press-gang gets you, you rat.

Very truly yours,

Rebecca Kazanjian,

Ruching Division,

Fournoutzis & Salmondy, Scrims and Valances.

Buffalos of the World, Unite!

*A*NYBODY who happened to be a buffalo in 1936 (or was supporting during his taxable year one or more buffalos closely dependent upon him) is going to have a pretty hollow feeling in the pit of his stomach when he gets a hinge at the July issue of *The Field*. In that excellent British sporting magazine, one "Old Harrow Boy" attacks the custom of shouting and waving the arms and hat to break up stampeding buffalos, and actually suggests *whistling* as a better means of dispersing unlawful assemblages of bison.

I hold no buff for the briefalo—I beg pardon, I should have said "I hold no brief for the buffalo," but I am too choked with rage about this matter to be very coherent. I have never taken money from any pro-bison organization and outside of a fatty deposit between the shoulder blades I am no more buffalo than you are. But of all the appalling, repellent, revolting and insupportable bits of *Schrecklichkeit* ever fobbed off on a lethargic public under the guise of sportsmanship, this is the absolute pay-off.

First, just who *is* this "Old Harrow Boy" anyway? I looked him up in the London Street directory but the only name like it was "O'Hara Roy, 15, Pig's Walk, Wapping Old Stairs." "Pig's Walk" is good; "Pig's Talk," if you ask *me*. A man who hasn't even got the nerve to sign his own name to a letter. Well, Mr. O'Hara, let us cast an eye over your record and see who it is that goes around lousing up a buffalo's good name. It might interest you to know that I sent a friend of mine around to Wapping Old Stairs to ask a few questions. I believe he came to your service flat one afternoon and talked to your "housekeeper." Bet you thought he was some kind of an idiot, eh? Well, he is. He's one of the most all-around idiots I know, but there's one thing about him. He doesn't spend his day teasing buffalos. He leaves that to a certain pig in Wapping Old Stairs. No need to mention names.

Among other things I was interested to learn that our precious Mr. O'Hara had been tried and convicted in Rhodesia for acting as *agent-provocateur* in an uprising of water buffalos in 1911. Shortly afterward three buffalos reported to the British High Commissioner at Elandfontein that they had been bored by Mr. O'Hara. The seriousness of the charge forced the Commissioner's hand, and an investigation was held. It revealed that O'Hara had approached the buffalos in a kind of hysterical, excited fashion and told them some rambling inconsequential story without any point. The bisons alleged boredom and petitioned for damages. I have been in correspondence with Sir Herbert Antinous (then Sir Herbert Antinous) who acted as medical officer in the case. He has been kind enough to forward me a transcript of the evidence together with a locket containing hair from one of the buffalos as proof. Here is Sir Herbert's version of the matter:

"I examined the three buffalos about an hour after they claimed Mr. O'Hara had bored them. They still bore the marks of their recent ordeal. One of them had a coated tongue and was feverish. The second seemed normal but slightly bemused. The third, however, had no tongue. I guess the cat got it. (*Laughter.*)

"*Question from Magistrate Nirdlinger:* Sir Herbert, kindly confine yourself to the case. What is the difference between a Florida orange and a letter?

"*Sir Herbert:* I don't know, Your Worship.

"*Sir Herbert:* Well, you'd be a hell of a man to send to mail a letter. Stand down."

At this point there was a commotion in court caused

by O'Hara's pitching forward out of the dock in a dead faint. The session was adjourned to allow Sir Herbert to examine the prisoner. Here is his version of the case:

"I examined O'Hara about five minutes after he pitched forward out of the dock in a dead faint. He still bore the marks of his recent ordeal. He had a coated tongue and was feverish."

The subsequent history of the case is completely without interest. The accused's counsel entered a plea of *prosit* and O'Hara was lashed to the mizzen and given five dozen with the cat, who seemed to be in good condition except for a slightly coated tongue.

This then is the man who advocates whistling at stampeding buffalos. This unctuous traitor, writing on foolscap in onion juice, who signs fictitious names to his slanders, dares undermine an institution as hollowed as waving one's hat at buffalos. Ever since the days of Buffoon the naturalist it has gone without saying that the first thing you do on seeing a buffalo is shout and wave your arms and hat. But no; that's not good enough for O'Hara. *He* has to put on side. *He* has to make a holy show out of himself in front of animals, let alone the Kaffir boys. And maybe you don't think the Kaffir boys talk! Only last night old man Kaffir and his youngest boy Morris came into a poolroom in Spion Kop. Morris had two beers and started talking. Well, sir, he talked pretty near two hours before they could stop him. I just mention this to show how the Kaffir boys talk once they get started.

Well, O'Hara, I've said my say. I'm a plain-spoken, grizzled old seadog, none of your French airs for old Peleg Starbuck. Why, bless your heart, boy, I was a powder monkey aboard the old Guerriere afore you was born. I've been a galley slave aboard the pirate proas of the Dey of Algiers, I've been shipwrecked among the head-hunting Dyaks, pursued by Arab dhows in the Straits of Aden, and careened in the Dry Tortugas. But don't you heed this old man's talk; you young folks go along and have a look through my spyglass. What's that you say—a suspicious moisture in my eye? Pshaw—a bit of rain, shiver my blini. And coughing to hide his embarrassment, old Peleg hobbled up the shell-decorated path to his cottage as Frederica and I spat reflectively on his peonies and turned our faces toward Ostable and the setting sun.

The Kiss Fool

When he told her about the other woman, her eyes
went from azure to blue and from Princeton
to Yale. Another fascinating instalment of
Helen and Rabbit Warren's married
life, in which the young couple
find readjustment in a
coal bunker

*M*ING TOY EPSTEIN shook out her glorious honey-colored hair and shrugged an insolent silken shoulder. The little group of co-eds gathered in her room looked at Ming Toy admiringly. She of all the girls of Voorhees College dared defy convention by rolling her stockings and puffing "swaggeroots," as she lightly termed them. Now, before the horrified yet fascinated eyes of her schoolmates, she extracted a package of Ziras and lit one.

"Have a coffin-nail?" she invited lazily. "There's some Hassans in the drawer there if you prefer them."

"No, thank you," replied Hope Kaufman, leader of the basketball team, coldly. "I don't indulge."

"Oh, fudge!" mocked Ming Toy disdainfully. "You're only young once, so what's the diff? Ish ka bibble, say I! Give me the old pagan philosophy every time:

[167]

STRICTLY FROM HUNGER

"Come fill the cup and in the fire of spring
The winter garment of repentance fling."

The girls looked at each other meaningfully; this must be a quotation from one of the "deep" books Ming Toy was always perusing. Yet Rumor had it that all of her knowledge was not derived from books. Only the night before, she had been seen by one of the men students in an amusement park of poor repute with a flashily dressed shoe salesman. So it was that a small delegation of the more sedate seniors had called on her today to remonstrate. Roberta Kaplan, spokeswoman for the group, put the question point-blank.

"Aren't you giving the college a bad name, Ming Toy?" she asked earnestly. "You were seen at Duby's Grove late last night without a chaperon and you didn't get in till four 'g.m.' "

"I'm old enough to take care of myself," Ming Toy interrupted defiantly. "I like a 'gazebo' with plenty of 'zip' and besides, Stacy Spewack has always been a perfect gentleman. He always blows me to swell eats and seems to have loads of ready mazuma."

"Mazuma?" queried one of the bolder girls disapprovingly.

"Kale—rhino—spondulix," enlightened Ming Toy, carelessly drawing a powder puff from her mesh bag and dabbing at her nose. She patted the wrinkles from her daringly short skirt, slipped on a raccoon coat and affixed a wicked little mouche to her saucy nose.

"Anybody going down to Turtletaub's?" she inquired innocently.

"No, and you had best not be seen there yourself," flared Liane Kornsweet acidly.

"Oh, beans!" called Ming Toy airily. "Don't take any wooden nickels, you bonehead!" Liane compressed her lips at this Parthian shot. There was a moment's silence after the door slammed; then the girls' voices rose in a hubbub of gossip.

"Is it true her parents are—*divorced?*" whispered Blossom Jaffe.

"Yes," declared Désirée Spitzer. "And what's more, they say she's immensely wealthy. She told me her mother promised her a Stanley Steamer if she passes her 'Ec' course!" A sigh of envy followed this announcement, for few of the loyal daughters of sleepy old Voorhees had ever ridden in a gleaming brass Stanley "auto." One unsophisticated "freshie" in particular listened with eyes like saucers. Blossom Jaffe, wishing to shock her, winked meaningfully at her fellows.

"I shouldn't wonder that Ming Toy has—gone the limit," she insinuated.

"That's a lie!" flared the freshie. "Why, she's never

driven more than fifteen miles per hour!" The girls' merriment echoed and resounded against the walls of hoary old Ascheim-Zondeck, for it was clear to all present that the freshie was still thinking of the Stanley Steamer.

Ming Toy Epstein, on the other hand, had laughingly dismissed the incident from her mind by the time she emerged from the dorm, for she was a typical New York girl, possessed of the gay spirit characteristic of the denizens of that swarming beehive of humanity. Her heart was full of Stacy Spewack that afternoon as she made her pert way down Pratt Street toward Turtletaub's. To think that this exclusive man-about-town bachelor with his distinguished gray temples and Bond Street clothes should have laid his heart at her feet! She hummed a snatch of melody and surveyed the carmine of her pouting lips.

" 'Lo, Ming!" She looked up to find "Chubby" Danziger, Voorhees' popular yell-leader, confronting her, arms akimbo. Her smile froze as she discerned Garish Cooper at his side, and she attempted to hurry on. Garish caught her sleeve imploringly.

"Won't you give me a chance to explain, Ming Toy?" he pleaded. "I wasn't kissing Truly Aronowitz the night of the Soph Hop, I . . ." She stiffened and was gone, leaving a much astonished "Chubby" staring after her.

"Br-r-r-r!" he commented humorously, turning up his coat collar and imitating an English "dude." "Pretty chilly around 'ere, eh what, old top?" Despite the rebuff Garish could not suppress a rueful smile at the other's mimicry as they turned toward their "frat" house for a "bull session."

In a private booth at Turtletaub's, Stacy Spewack lifted a cynical, worldly eyebrow as he bent over Ming Toy's hand and kissed it in his usual Continental fashion.

"But—but I thought you promised to take me to tea?" faltered Ming Toy.

"Cara mia, eet is impossible," he shrugged, his monocle glittering. "Business—business—mon Doo, do you Americans think of nothing else? Ah, one day you and I—we steal away to a little villa in San Remo, yes?" The infinite caress of Ming Toy's glance was his answer. A look of cunning invaded Spewack's eye. "Wednesday I must leave for the Cleveland territory—you will dine weeth me tonight—alone?"

The spring night was like heady wine in the patio of El Weltschmerz; a young May moon dreamed above Blumenthal's Five as they dispensed the rich strains of *Floating on the Bay at Tripoli* and *Ma, He's Makin' Eyes at Me*. In a cozy room upstairs genial red-faced Tony Barracuda beamed as he filled Ming Toy's slender-stemmed glass with the bubbling Médoc. Then, at a sharp glance from the silver-haired Spewack, he winked mightily and tiptoed out discreetly.

"Thees night—eet is made for love, no?" began Stacy, his eyes feasting hungrily on the slender young shoulders opposite him. And well he might, for Ming Toy was radiant tonight, a vision of loveliness in orange and silver tulle, the daring décolleté bodice fringed with dainty peplums fresh from the Rue de la Paix. Her wistful beauty caught at his throat as she tapped him coquettishly with her fan.

"Every dog returns to his . . . I mean, what's one man's meat is another's poison," she parried. Suddenly she was a little girl, infinitely desirable, with great tragic eyes from which mirth had died. He was by her side now, was Stacy Spewack, looking into the very heart of her.

"You haf some other sweetheart, *peut-être?*" he probed. So must have smiled some ravening Sumatra tiger watching from the edge of the jungle a graceful startled gazelle by a watercourse. Ming Toy shook her head. "Listen," continued Stacy, drawing her nearer to him. "Your mother—she is rich?"

"Oh, don't worry about money," dismissed Ming Toy, draining her glass and tapping a cigarette on the back of her hand. "Mother has oodles."

"Thees—how you say—oodles—eet is serious?" asked Spewack. "I know a surgeon in Vienna . . ."

"Oh, silly!" She laughed, the curve of her throat flung back and little lights dancing in her eyes. Then, as some calm lake is rippled by a sudden summer storm, she snuggled closer to him and shivered.

"Oh, Stacy," she murmured, "put your arms around me—hold me close! I've been on my own since I was fifteen."

"Own?" he repeated dully. "Own what?"

"Never mind, you beast," she stopped him. But he, fiery Latin, was not to be so lightly dissuaded. His hands caught at her.

"Stacy!" she reproved. "That look in your eyes—oh!" She was pounding at the unyielding steel of his chest as his hands groped for her. Of what avail those childish fingers before this goatish ogre with red-rimmed eyes? Her strength was ebbing.

The door burst in with a rending crash of woodwork as Garish Cooper met Stacy Spewack with flailing fists. Spewack grunted; the first blow had told, and already youth's flaunting banners were storming the citadel of age and pampered living. Knuckles of iron with the drive of steam pistons behind them hammered at the aged playboy's jowls and he was on the floor, weakly holding up his pants for mercy.

"Hands up, Mr. Slippery Jacobs!" Garish wheeled, stunned. Ming Toy Epstein, a resolute little figure in a simple tailored suit, was presenting a businesslike revolver to Stacy's temple. The latter went white by turns.

"You—you know me then?" he stammered.

"I never forget the face of a crook," came her even tones. In the same gesture she slipped a pair of manacles over the prostrate clubman's wrists and turned, revealing a shiny steel badge pinned to her blouse. Garish gaped at her.

"Louise Wasservogel, U. S. Secret Service," she said quietly. "This man is wanted in Washington for the theft of the Z—— documents. I owe you a debt of thanks; you arrived just in the nick of time, Monsieur—"

"Gaston Vernissage, mademoiselle, of the Parisian police," bowed the young man. "Papa Crudeau of the Sûreté will never forget what you have done tonight."

But there is one chapter which you will not find in Papa Crudeau's memoirs, and that is still being written in a sunny garden in Surrey amid the drone of bees, where Madame Louise Vernissage, alias Ming Toy Epstein, smiles fondly at her husband Gaston, alias Garish Cooper. Already two fair-haired laughing tots have blessed their union, and flies gather from near and far to watch them frisk with a basket of puppies. Spec, the Saint Bernard, now grown old, lies contentedly in the sun and fondly allows them to play with her children, for she, wise dog, knows that

Like sandals tracing love's sweet message in the sand,
We stop, we live, we laugh and dance the sarabande.

The Infant Industry

*U*P UNTIL the late delivery yesterday afternoon I had always been an admirer of Postmaster General Jim Farley. I suppose I was just a romantic little fool, but I pictured him behind a wicket somewhere in Washington helpfully retying the string on my parcels, chuckling appreciatively over my change-of-address cards, and burning an occasional obscene bookseller. It became something of a crush (all on my side, of course), and for a time I even wore a locket containing some of his former hair. I don't know why I'm telling you all this, but my cheeks burn when I think of the things I did. For instance, that rumor about him tasting every single stamp before it was sold, to make sure it wasn't poisoned. I spread that. I took to using "Farley" as a superlative; if I said "Jeekers! Isn't that sunset too Farley for *words?*"

you knew right away I meant it was a peacherino. Man, I was simply "batsy" about that Farley! He just couldn't do a wrong thing.

So you can imagine how I felt when the postman rang my bell yesterday with that package from the Chalmers Publishing Company. I don't care how crowded the United States mails are; it shouldn't take twenty-four years for a copy of *Technique of the Photoplay*, by Epes Winthrop Sargent (copyright 1913), to reach me, of all people. The janitor warned me when I took this apartment on Fifty-sixth Street that the reception was bad, but I was too full of Farley to listen.

Not that Mr. Sargent's little book wasn't worth waiting for, mind you. His manual contains 182 pages of sprightly information for what used to be called a "photoplaywright" in 1913 but is now referred to variously as "scenario-writer," "scenarist," or just plain "overpaid slob." As one reads it after a quarter of a century, *Technique of the Photoplay* leaves one heavy with nostalgia. The names of Vitagraph, Lubin, Kalem, Essanay, Reliance, and Imp recall serials like *The Iron Claw* and the satisfaction of inserting nickels in those chocolate-vending machines on the backs of the seats just to hear the ensuing crash. It is so long since I was sprayed with orange essence by an usher that I had begun to believe I read it somewhere in Proust. Mr. Sargent throws everything into sharp focus again, but here and there his otherwise seaworthy craft springs a leak.

To begin with, in Chapter IV, "Tools of the Trade," the author tells us, "A manuscript written on butcher's wrapping paper in red ink may be a literary gem, but as a rule it's unlikely that the script will repay reading and so it will be passed over." Speaking from some slight experience, I must break with Mr. Sargent right there. The only scripts of mine which ever got themselves produced were on butcher's wrapping paper in red ink. *Mutiny on the Bounty*, a picture I had nothing to do with and which was successful for that reason, was written on butcher's wrapping paper in red ink. *The Informer*, I am told, was written in a butcher shop, and unless Mr. Dudley Nichols tattooed it on a leg of veal, he must have used the only other materials at hand— butcher's wrapping paper and the inevitable red ink. I have tried writing motion-picture scripts on every other form of paper known, including paper towels, but without success. In an effort to bewitch my producers, I even tried Kleenex at one point. Kleenex makes a rather bulky script and sheds slightly during reading, but is very useful for actresses when they are trying to get up in a part, especially if you send along a jar of cold cream.

"The Unmasked Question" is the title of Chapter XXVIII, and in it Mr. Sargent poses a number of questions likely to perplex the tyro at this trade, such as "Do they have to wait until it rains to make pictures in the rain?" and "What does it mean when I receive a script without even a rejection slip?" Mr. Sargent manages to answer these very well without any help from me, but he flounders badly when he gets to the financial end. To the query "Should I mark a price on my script?" he replies carelessly, flicking an infinitesimal speck of ash from his waistcoat, "If you wish to. Most authors find it more profitable to leave the price to the editor." I must say I don't see why Mr. Sargent has to go so damn *fin-de-siècle* all of a sudden; we're not in the Domino Room of the Café Royal, my friend. A man asks you a simple question, and you languidly sniff the sunflower in your buttonhole and dismiss him with a phony epigram. Well, Mr. Art-for-Art's-Sake, *I* always mark a price on my scripts; I mark "a million dollars" in good big letters on the wrapper, and sometimes I even say "a million *million* dollars." I don't say I always get it, but they know they're dealing with a high-grade man. Ho, ho—you don't catch my scripts coming back without even a rejection slip!

"Suppose," runs another question, "that my script calls for some article that I possess and the studio is not likely to have. Should it be sent with the script?" Mr. Sargent becomes quite snappish: "Simply state that you have such an article and would be pleased to loan it on request.

Do not send it until you are positively asked for it." It's Mr. Sargent's affair if he wants to make up nice mild questions and then answer them in a rage, but he's courting schizophrenia. Personally, I think that if you wrote a story about sextuplets and you happened to have sextuplets around the house, you'd be a fine fool not to send them along with the script. On the other hand, if your story was about a pair of blucher shoes or a Nesselrode pudding, it wouldn't be necessary. I mean the story wouldn't be necessary; just make a neat bundle of the shoes, mark it "a million *million* dollars," and send it off to Hollywood parcel post. And don't be too surprised when you see them turn up on the feet of a certain Postmaster General whose last name rhymes with "barley." (No need to mention names.)

The Case of Colonel Bradshaw

*A*BOUT four months ago, in the columns of an English sporting magazine, one ran across a perfectly astounding story about a certain Lieutenant-Colonel Bradshaw, retired, of the Royal Engineers, and his experiments with trout. The details were so amazing that the present writer was catapulted into a deep sleep from which he did not awake until fully fourteen hours later. A thick hedge had sprung up meanwhile around his enchanted castle, and had it not been for the handsome prince thundering at the door to read the gas meter, he might still be in thrall to the wicked fairy. Unfortunately, the name of the sporting magazine evaded his memory the following day, and since his home was littered with English sporting magazines, he was unable to recover the item. He at once entered into correspondence with a friend of his who is pretty high up in Fortnum & Mason's—chief of the strawberry-jam division, in fact—and had him look up the case. He has just received a complete dossier from abroad, and if you can only keep that foot of yours from its restless tapping, the entire city ought to be blanketed in sleep by this week-end at the latest.

Lieutenant-Colonel Desmond H. R. Bradshaw, F.R.G.S. and Gartersnapper in Ordinary, had been invalided home from one of the minor Indian hill wars. He was living quietly at Fosley-over-Satchmouth in Hants, a bull of a man with a face the color of teak, and a fierce white imperial. His sole servant, an Annamite boy named Nebich, took care of the villa with the aid of a char who came in. Forty years of curry and brandy-and-soda had given the Colonel the burnish of a copper jug and third ranking blood pressure in the Empire. He had already had one stroke and was leisurely awaiting the next. Still athletic, he occasionally distinguished himself in competition with a score of other retired colonels by his ability to snort and rustle the *Morning Post* louder than the rest. His snug personal fortune of a little less than two million pounds was invested in Consols and he was honorary chairman of the Widows' and Orphans' Bank in the City. The sunny silence of "The Whelps" was only disturbed by the hum of bees and the sporadic whiplike report of a hardening artery.

THE CASE OF COLONEL BRADSHAW

Always an enthusiastic trout fisherman, the Colonel collected his gear one fine May morning and went for a stroll with his pipe. Whistling a raffish tune, he soon found himself a secluded bank of his favorite stream. He had selected a fly from his case and was preparing to cast when an extraordinary idea occurred to him. What would the fly look like to the trout? What did he himself look like to a trout? What, in fact, did *anything* look like to trout?

The impact of an idea on virgin territory immediately aroused a salvo of protest from the Colonel's arteries; he turned a darker red than ever and wondered whether he was about to faint. "Felt a bit liverish" runs the entry in his journal for that day. At luncheon, his listlessness frightened the Annamite boy. His master had forgotten to kick him on entering and ate only two plates of curry. Over the fourth brandy-and-soda, Bradshaw made up his mind to go to the bottom of the trout matter, literally if necessary.

That afternoon the Colonel spent almost an hour lying motionless in the bed of a shallow stream, breathing through a reed. All he was able to see was a brownish murk and an old boot. The trout showed no desire to fraternize. "By Gad, sir!" he shouted at Nebich that night, "the country's going to the demnition bowwows! I'll show the beggars tomorrow!" Bootjack in hand, he terrified the Annamite into daubing speckled colors on the Colonel's jowls and shoulders. At sunrise the latter hid himself in a shady pool and waited for anglers. Three hours later, a boy fishing with a bent pin saw the pseudo-trout and made off screaming. In his panic Bradshaw burrowed into the mud and caught his foot in a clump of rushes. He escaped with his life, but through bad timing encountered the postman as he regained his villa. The sight of the Colonel, who by now looked less like a rainbow trout than a mandrill, turned the postman to stone. He still stands on the lawn of "The Whelps," his bag stuffed with little stone envelopes and parcels; the present owners are considering turning him into a fountain.

The Annamite boy had busied himself that afternoon sharpening a cleaver with which to defend himself from a sortie by his employer, but he was unprepared for what followed. The Colonel swept aside the evening curry with a trembling hand and ordered Nebich to produce a dish of grubs, minnows, and water bugs. The servant made his escape by the back door, sought out the constable of Folsey-over-Satchmouth, and put himself in protective custody. Lieutenant-Colonel Bradshaw made an indifferent meal off several bits of red flannel and a Parmachenee Belle. For the first night in his life he had no relish for the *Court Circular*, but sat brooding before the fireplace until long past bedtime.

THE CASE OF COLONEL BRADSHAW

The fact that the Colonel left no note announcing his plans made the work of the inquest doubly difficult, but the testimony of an eyewitness may help piece together the tragedy. About eleven the next morning, Job Humphrey, Lord Lethal's gamekeeper, sauntering gun in hand by the River Eft, saw something like a huge salmon, but with arms instead of fins, trying to leap a rapid on its way upstream. It was generally conceded that Humphrey must have been drunk at the time, for he maintained stoutly that the fish was swearing like an ostler. In any event, the man's defense—that he thought it was the Loch Lomond sea serpent bound inland—must be accepted, for he obviously never would have fired two express loads into Lieutenant-Colonel Bradshaw on a whim. Altogether, it was a regrettable incident, more so since it gave prominent Laborites in the House of Commons last week an opportunity to rise on the question "Are we facing revolution?" and attack Tories who bequeath two million pounds to study the mental processes of trout.

Waiting for Santy

A CHRISTMAS PLAYLET

Scene: The sweatshop of S. Claus, a manufacturer of children's toys, on North Pole Street. Time: The night before Christmas.

At rise, seven gnomes, Rankin, Panken, Rivkin, Riskin, Ruskin, Briskin, and Praskin, are discovered working furiously to fill orders piling up at stage right. The whir of lathes, the hum of motors, and the hiss of drying lacquer are so deafening that at times the dialogue cannot be heard, which is very vexing if you vex easily. (Note: The parts of Rankin, Panken, Rivkin, Riskin, Ruskin, Briskin, and Praskin are interchangeable, and may be secured directly from your dealer or the factory.)

$\mathcal{R}$ISKIN (*filing a Meccano girder, bitterly*)—
A parasite, a leech, a bloodsucker—altogether a five-star
no-goodnick! Starvation wages we get so he can ride
around in a red team with reindeers!

RUSKIN (*jeering*)—Hey, Karl Marx, whyn'tcha hire a
hall?

RISKIN (*sneering*)—Scab! Stool pigeon! Company spy!
(*They tangle and rain blows on each other. While waiting for these to dry, each returns to his respective task.*)

BRISKIN (*sadly, to Panken*)—All day long I'm painting
"Snow Queen" on these Flexible Flyers and my little
Irving lays in a cold tenement with the gout.

PANKEN—You said before it was the mumps.

BRISKIN (*with a fatalistic shrug*)—The mumps—the
Gout—go argue with City Hall.

[193]

PANKEN (*kindly, passing him a bowl*)—Here, take a piece fruit.

BRISKIN (*chewing*)—It ain't bad, for wax fruit.

PANKEN (*with pride*)—I painted it myself.

BRISKIN (*rejecting the fruit*)—Ptoo! Slave psychology!

RIVKIN (*suddenly, half to himself, half to the Party*)—I got a belly full of stars, baby. You make me feel like I swallowed a Roman candle.

PRASKIN (*curiously*)—What's wrong with the kid?

RISKIN—What's wrong with all of us? The system! Two years he and Claus's daughter's been making goo-goo eyes behind the old man's back.

PRASKIN—So what?

RISKIN (*scornfully*)—So what? Economic determinism! What do you think the kid's name is—J. Pierpont Rivkin? He ain't even got for a bottle Dr. Brown's Celery Tonic. I tell you, it's like gall in my mouth two young people shouldn't have a room where they could make great music.

RANKIN (*warningly*)—Shhh! Here she comes now! (*Stella Claus enters, carrying a portable phonograph. She and Rivkin embrace, place a record on the turntable, and begin a very slow waltz, unmindful that the phonograph is playing "Cohen on the Telephone."*)

STELLA (*dreamily*)—Love me, sugar?

RIVKIN—I can't sleep, I can't eat, that's how I love you.

[194]

You're a double malted with two scoops of whipped cream; you're the moon rising over Mosholu Parkway; you're a two weeks' vacation at Camp Nitgedaiget! I'd pull down the Chrysler Building to make a bobbie pin for your hair!

STELLA—I've got a stomach full of anguish. Oh, Rivvy, what'll we do?

PANKEN (sympathetically)—Here, try a piece fruit.

RIVKIN (fiercely)—Wax fruit—that's been my whole life! Imitations! Substitutes! Well, I'm through! Stella, tonight I'm telling your old man. He can't play mumblety-peg with two human beings! (The tinkle of sleigh bells is heard offstage, followed by a voice shouting, "Whoa, Dasher! Whoa, Dancer!" A moment later S. Claus enters in a gust of mock snow. He is a pompous bourgeois of sixty-five who affects a white beard and a false air of benevolence. But tonight the ruddy color is missing from his cheeks, his step falters, and he moves heavily. The gnomes hastily replace the marzipan they have been filching.)

STELLA (anxiously)—Papa! What did the specialist say?

Claus (brokenly)—The biggest professor in the country . . . the best cardiac man that money could buy. . . . I tell you I was like a wild man.

STELLA—Pull yourself together, Sam!

CLAUS—It's no use. Adhesions, diabetes, sleeping sick-

[195]

ness, decalcomania—oh, my God! I got to cut out climbing in chimneys, he says—me, Sanford Claus, the biggest toy concern in the world!

STELLA (*soothingly*)—After all, it's only one man's opinion.

CLAUS—No, no, he cooked my goose. I'm like a broken uke after a Yosian picnic. Rivkin!

RIVKIN—Yes, Sam.

CLAUS—My boy, I had my eye on you for a long time. You and Stella thought you were too foxy for an old man, didn't you? Well, let bygones be bygones. Stella, do you love this gnome?

STELLA (*simply*)—He's the whole stage show at the Music Hall, Papa; he's Toscanini conducting Beethoven's Fifth; he's—

CLAUS (*curtly*)—Enough already. Take him. From now on he's a partner in the firm. (*As all exclaim, Claus holds up his hand for silence.*) And tonight he can take my route and make the deliveries. It's the least I could do for my own flesh and blood. (*As the happy couple kiss, Claus wipes away a suspicious moisture and turns to the other gnomes.*) Boys, do you know what day tomorrow is?

GNOMES (*crowding around expectantly*)—Christmas!

CLAUS—Correct. When you look in your envelopes tonight, you'll find a little present from me—a forty-percent pay cut. And the first one who opens his trap—gets this.

WAITING FOR SANTY

(As he holds up a tear-gas bomb and beams at them, the gnomes utter cries of joy, join hands, and dance around him shouting exultantly. All except Riskin and Briskin, that is, who exchange a quick glance and go underground.)

CURTAIN

Dinner Party

*A*T EIGHT o'clock it was almost dark and Wilshire Boulevard was choked with cars rushing toward the early stage shows in Los Angeles. The reek of gasoline and frying rubber grew heavier. Blocks away the Warner Western Theater, a cheese dream the color of a chlorinated swimming pool, guarded its little brood of Dutch windmills, barbecued-beef pits, and pagoda gas stations. An inverted ice cream cone labeled "Hackett's, The Home of Hot Nuts" was having its formal opening at LaBrea; the electricians focusing the Kliegs on it looked hot and tired. Ahead of me the Feldman's Farina sign which meant South Ciolito Avenue grew larger. Waiting in the left-hand traffic lane to make the turn, I marveled at the neon salesman who had converted a desert trail into the most hideous thoroughfare in America. The traffic broke momentarily and I slid

through slickly landscaped darkness into the celotex haci-
endas and Dennison crepe-paper chateaux of South
Ciolito Avenue.

One of the first things Barbara Teagler did after her
husband signed a contract at Metro-Goldwyn-Mayer was
to cement their social position by renting an enormous
Italian renaissance palace on South Ciolito Avenue. The
lady who had conceived and brought forth this extrava-
gant building had fallen into the hands of the Pacific
Finance Company. Consequently, for a small monthly
payment of four hundred dollars, the Teaglers were per-
mitted to receive their milk and mail at an address which,
the renting agent assured them, was second to none.

The house was dreary and foolish, the living room, or
hall, so large and full of shadows that people took to
huddling in the center of it and glancing hurriedly over
their shoulders. It was lit entirely by wax tapers with a
funny smell that stayed in your clothes for hours. There
were four or five portraits of grim-looking men on the
walls, and sometimes, when the Capehart was playing a
quiet passage from Sibelius, you began to feel that the
eyes in the portraits were watching you. So it was no
wonder that a story got around that Barbara Teagler was
a poisoner, especially since she always wore a peculiar
large ring on her third left finger. I don't suppose it was

really hollow at all, but I was always very careful to see that I took my drinks directly from the Filipino without letting Barbara handle them.

What made the poison theory ridiculous was that the Teaglers made no bones about it—they poisoned right out in the open, so to speak. When you went to dinner there, you drank martinis out of small pewter cups. Three of these produced a condition similar to the bends. If you managed to get to the dinner table under your own power and could still remember your name, you knew you were drunk on metal polish. But the Teaglers had only begun with you.

Most people get very patriotic about whatever they live with, whether it is their wives, their furniture, or their clothing. Barbara and Walter Teagler had not decorated their dining room but they endorsed it completely. The table—Walter called it "the festal board"—was almost twenty feet long. It was a little too high to eat from comfortably, and you had to reach up to place your elbows on it. With the food practically at eye level, and the guest fighting to keep awake in the semi-darkness, dining became a matter of stoking the frame and to hell with the little niceties.

It was turkey, inevitably; the Teaglers always served turkey, just as they always expected to receive turkey when they ate at the homes of other members of the movie colony. Barbara Teagler would sooner have come down to dinner in her step-ins than ask people in to dine on any bird less opulent than turkey. To Barbara, who had bridged the gap in the social hierarchy between show-girl in Warner musicals and wife of an executive, turkey was the one unassailable indication of entrenched wealth. After that in close order came mink coats, diamonds, and Duesenbergs. I was staring at her tightly marceled hair and wondering how so regal a creature had ever come out of Scranton, Pennsylvania, when I saw she was giving me her most reproachful glance.

"You're not touching your wild rice," she pouted. "What's the matter, aren't you hungry?"

I immediately represented that I was famished and made a great show of wolfing my wild rice until I felt her eyes wander. The truth was that the metal polish cocktails had given me a slight headache, which was not being helped by the small talk of my immediate neighbor, Byron Siegel. Siegel, one of the more prosperous agents in the industry, was engaged in an analysis of the current pictures. He was a stout, swarthy man who had made a great deal of money by being positive about probabilities.

"It stinks," he was telling Walter Teagler in his hoarse voice. "I tell you it won't get buttons at the box-office. All right, I grant you they made it for spit, a hundred and eighty g's. But it's too smart for the small towns. New York, yes; maybe Chicago, one or two others. But you think those cowboys ever heard of Noel Coward?"

He almost upset a goblet in his passionate scorn. Walter, at loss for an argument before these hard certainties, was preparing to light the cigar which was an integral part of his face when the Filipino appeared with the dessert. Mrs. Siegel, a sharp-featured brunette glittering with arrogance and an incredible number of bracelets, helped herself to the elaborately tinted and sculptured ice cream without missing a beat in her report of a recent scandal.

"All the time Edman's playing around with this script girl," she told Barbara with relish. "Why, Lucille Edman was carrying on afternoons with this here bit player, Jack something—I forget his name. My dear, it was too SORBID. And then the pay-off is that this Jack goes and steals Edman's picture at the preview! Everybody was raving about him at the Troc and Lucille just sat there and played dumb." She uttered a short savage laugh at Lucille's hypocrisy and spooned in a large measure of ice cream.

"Is that marvelous?" demanded Byron of Walter and myself with rising intensity, "IS THAT MARVELOUS? If you saw it in a picture you wouldn't believe it. Edman was nuts when he found out."

"She got a good settlement out of him," Mrs. Siegel commented practically.

"Don't worry about Lucille. She had him pegged for a soft touch from the beginning," said her husband. "Edman was always a set-up for dames. Say, didn't I know Lucille back in the old silent days? But it didn't do no good to tell him she was a tramp—he has to go and marry her yet."

"Wasn't that her mother—the one that got her face lifted?" asked Mrs. Siegel suddenly.

"What face lifted?" Siegel turned on his wife with the look of contemptuous distaste her questions always provoked in him.

"Oh, you know! She had her face lifted and the man from the filling station . . ." Siegel's frown of concentration vanished, but was immediately replaced by extreme irritation.

"Now for Christ's sake, don't ruin a gag," he implored. "Anything I hate is somebody . . ."

"Then you tell it," Mrs. Siegel retorted angrily. "You ought to know it. You been telling it for the last ten years."

"Yes, Byron, you tell it," encouraged Barbara Teagler, bending forward with the parted lips and assumed interest of the hostess aware she had not been listening. Privately she had been wondering whether the meal was sumptuous enough for a man of Siegel's caliber; he had given no signs of discomfort or made light references to bicarbonate of soda.

"Well," began Siegel, mollified, "this'll kill you." He signaled to the Filipino. "Make mine a large cup, Moto. This Lucille we're talking about's mother was one of these dames about forty-one, forty-two. She used to be in pictures herself, but years ago, when Bessie Barriscale and Louise Glaum were big. So Lucille's in New York in the Scandals and her mother's living over here in one of these little studio dumps. She ain't bad-looking, but from years of using that make-up, why she's kind of wrinkled and don't get the play she used to from the boys. Her hair—" He took a quick look at Barbara's sleek blond hair and changed quickly. "What I mean is, she always goes around wearing slacks and still trying to be cute, but it's too late. There's a guy at the filling station down the corner she's got a yen for, one of those big husky dopes that's always giving out with the personality, figures maybe somebody'll give him a break in pictures. She gives him the come-on every day, but an old lady like that he don't know from nothing.

"Well, one thing and another, and before you know it, the old dame figures herself an angle. She goes down to L.A. to one of those muggs that advertise in the papers and they give her face a going-over. I didn't see her but she came in the office one day and my secretary said you wouldn't know her. It must of made a difference to this lug at the filling station, because right away he started on the make."

Mrs. Siegel's face wore the strained and virtuous smirk of one who knows the point; occasionally she gave Barbara, Walter and myself birdlike little glances and chuckled. Her husband inhaled his cigar, blew the smoke out judicially, and took a sip of coffee to indicate that he was in a position to abuse our attention.

"Well, they kid back and forth, and pretty soon she says how about coming up to her joint that night for a highball and some laughs. He figures it's okey-doke. Well, when he gets there, she's got the gas log going in the fireplace and everything set for a big time. They have some drinks. The kid says something about it's too warm and is going to shut off the gas heater, but she says no, it's cozy that way, and have another drink. He don't mind, and pretty soon he's spilling the story of his life. She eats it up and tells him he reminds her of Gable, only more manly, which is duck soup for him. All this time it's getting warmer in the flat, till finally he can't stand it. He turns to her to say he's going to shut off the gas, and takes one look. Then he busts out laughing. She says what's the matter, but he can't stop; he just grabs his hat and scrams. She can hear him screaming all the way downstairs. So she runs in the bedroom to find her mirror."

He paused, waiting for the question he knew would come from Barbara Teagler.

"What was it, Byron?" For a moment the turkey was forgotten.

"Why, the heat," he explained softly, "the gas heat. It melted all that paraffin in her face where they'd lifted it, and her chin had kind of run down in a point and her cheeks were sagging—"

"Ugh," said Mrs. Siegel. "Never mind, we know."

"Is that dynamite or IS THAT DYNAMITE?" inquired Siegel.

"Nice people," remarked Barbara Teagler. "Moto, serve the leekoors in the living room."

Seedlings of Desire

$\mathcal{B}$RENT CARSTAIRS, Broadway's foremost producer, lifted a bored black eyebrow in languid amusement and bestowed a tolerant stare through sleepy eyelids on Moot Point, his general manager. His long, sensitive fingers, the fingers of a poet and dreamer he had recently acquired at auction, toyed with the skull of a soubrette which served him as a paperweight.

"This little—ah—stock actress of yours is all very well," he threw at Point, "but can't you see, Moot, the part calls for a woman of the world. . . ."

"Ach, *mein Gott!*" groaned Point in his comical German dialect, flinging his toupee on the rug and stamping on it. "He calls Gaby Birnbaum a stock actress! I tell you, Brent, nefer haf I seen such youth, such fire, such . . ." Carstairs exchanged a quizzical glance with his Japanese manservant, fitted it into an ivory holder and lit it abstractedly. A muscle flickered in his lean jaw, and as its sound died out in the great room, Carstairs arose.

"All right, Moot, I'll see her," he said decisively. "Pack my bags, Homo. I'm leaving immediately for Wilkes-Barre."

"Shall I pack your flannels, sair?" queried the inscrutable Oriental.

"No, never mind them," waved Carstairs irritably. It was characteristic of the man that he usually ate a few swatches of flannel whilst traveling on trains. But today he was nervous, distraught; with the opening of *Becky's Blintzes* scarcely a week off and no leading woman in view, he had even left a plate of tasty green billiard felt untouched at breakfast. Homo shook his head and went off muttering indignantly.

"Faix, and it's th' divil a bit he's been afther eatin'," Homo thought to himself. "Th' loikes av thim shpalpeen play-acthors traipsin' in ivry hour av th' day an' noight a man'd gang fair daft, begorra!" And with many a rueful shake of his head, the faithful old darky retainer began to prepare for his master's journey.

Gaby Birnbaum gave her saucy little nose an extra fillip with the powder puff and threw herself a final admiring glance in the mirror. She saw there a retroussé nose and across its bridge a dash of freckles; the next instant they were gone, without even bothering to close the door behind them. Old Pop, the stage-door watch-man, beamed admiringly as she stripped off her street clothes and buckled on the Carnegie foundation which enhanced her lissom figure.

"Some feller from the city out in front tonight, Gaby," confided the old gaffer mysteriously, sucking on his corn-pone with toothless gums. "Cal'late ez how yew won't be with us much longer."

"Why, Pop!" chided Gaby with a merry twinkle. "Who'd want poor little me in New York? I'd be so frightened. . . ."

"Your cue, Gaby!" She snatched up a long rope of artificial pears and strung them about the fluted column of her neck with a gay little laugh. Then, with pounding heart, she raced down the winding iron stairway and took her place in the wings. The opening chorus was just swelling from the orchestra:

We greet you tonight with hearts that are light
At the Wilkes-Barre Boat Club Show,
We know you'll enjoy all the jokes we employ,
For they're all quite new, you know;
Singing, dancing, hearts entrancing,
Fascinating, captivating boys are we, are we. . . .

[215]

From the first moment Brent Carstairs descried Gaby Birnbaum he could not help placing her on a pedestal and fumigating her. Only nineteen, there was still a sort of silken luster about her which fell to her knees in undulating folds. On her dainty egg-shaped head was massed a crop of auburn curls; the cucumbers she had grown there the previous summer were forgotten in the pulsing rhythm of the moment. There was that about Gaby playing *Cigarette* in *Under Two Flags* which would have moved even the stoniest eye to tears. Suffice it to say that when the curtain fell on the last act, in which *Cigarette* goes to face the firing-squad amid a fanfaronade of shoe-horns, Carstairs' decision was sealed.

"Then we may expect you Friday morning?" Brent Carstairs' voice was crisp as he folded the signed contract and stowed it into his plaid-back ulster.

"Y-yes," stammered Gaby. A blush mantled her cheek as the courtly impresario stooped and kissed her hand in two-four time. Long after he had gone she sat staring at his elegantly engraved card. Brent Carstairs! The name swam before her eyes; as she watched, it dove off the springboard, floated on its back and came up with a gold watch in its teeth. Ah, youth, youth! Canst thy bright pennons embossed with Hope's heraldry survive the blasts of the winter of thy discontent? The words of the immortal poet Peabody came back to her in their full poignancy.

Gaby Birnbaum stood in the swirling confusion of Grand Central hugging her shabby portmanteau to her. Wilkes-Barre was far behind now; she had burned her boats, and the first step was to hunt up a doctor to prescribe a soothing lotion for them. This done, Gaby repaired to a nearby eating-house and made a delicious breakfast of oatcreel and meap, flanked by hot hiscuits and bunny. Sluicing down her tired feet with a steaming draught of coffee, Gaby hurried to the offices of Brent Carstairs. The distinguished producer looked up from slitting his morning mail. A pleasant smile played around the corners of his desk.

"Well, Miss Minx," he began with mock severity, "are you ready for work—hard work? How are your muscles?" He gave her calf a playful squeeze.

"I—I forgot to bring them along," faltered Gaby, coloring violently.

"You must send for them instanter," directed Carstairs. "We don't want any shirkers in *Becky's Blintzes*, Miss Birnbaum. I think you had better begin your fencing lessons immediately." He pressed one of the buttons on his vest and "Mops," the red-headed but irrepressible office-boy, entered.

"Take this young lady over to Beppo for a fencing lesson," he ordered. "Oh, by the way, Miss Birnbaum, have you found quarters yet? No? Let me see—you had better use these for the time being." He handed her a roll of quarters and stood up. Gaby attempted to thank him, but her fingers were all thumbs. Carstairs rubbed a blue and freshly shaven cheek against her soft one and returned it to his coat-pocket.

"Now run along to your fencing lesson, child."

All that afternoon, under Beppo's watchful supervision, Gaby learned something of the art of fencing; how to drill the holes, the proper way to string barbed wire and, finally, a few choice dirty words to write on board fences. The next day, under the able guidance of Abel Guydens, Carstairs' dance director, she was initiated into the mysteries of Terpsichore. Each night she rubbed her aching back with Arnica, her colored maid, in close attendance. Mealtimes were spent closely scanning her lines. Every time he scanned them Brent Carstairs felt surer that he had not made a mistake. Within a week he gave up eating altogether and was spending his entire lunch hour just scanning her lines.

The opening night of *Becky's Blintzes* repaid his faith

in Gaby Birnbaum. She was vivid, vibrant, as sure-footed as a mountain goat. All her entrances were timed to the minute, and twice when she spoke a hush fell over the house and had to be removed by the ushers. Slowly the disbelief faded from the faces of the critics and was replaced by a placidity, a tenderness so intense that it could only be called slumber. For three minutes after the curtain no sound could be heard. Carstairs, astute *entrepreneur* that he was, finally sent the stagehands through the audience beating tin pans. Then at last jaded and blasé New York first nighters were thrilled to the core. A great reverberating snore rolled like a mighty wave from the mezzanine and broke at Gaby's feet. On its surface floated odds and ends of vegetables, stewed fruit and bits of pork fat. Not since the elder Kean had Gotham seen such an ovation. Gaby, flinging her bouquet of cardiac roses to the theatergoers, kissed her hand prettily to the boxes and withdrew to the flies, who were eagerly buzzing about her in admiration. Brent Carstairs was waiting, flushed and triumphant. In vain rival producers hammered on the door with tempting contracts; red-faced advertising men, their eyes bloodshot from too good living, stormed her dressing-room with sample jars of cold cream for endorsement. But it was useless—New York's most sought-after actress had vanished into thin air.

Fifteen miles away and four hours later, on the deck of Carstairs' private yacht, Gaby and Brent faced each other over the coffee-cups. In the distance twinkled the yellow lights of Long Island. Occasionally a girl's giggle would float faintly to them on the off-shore breeze and they would dip it in melted butter, eating it with eyes fixed on each other. At length Carstairs' voice, hoarse with passion, broke the silence.

"You remember our bargain?" he asked. There was a gleam in his small piggish eyes now which frightened her; she arose impulsively and went to the rail, drinking in the beauty of the night and attempting to marshal her thoughts. Brent's voice was at her elbow now, caressing it.

"Why do you repulse me, Gaby baby?" he begged. "You've been as cold-blooded as a fisk lately."

"Have I? Then it's time for you to retire," she told him with desperate gayety. He uttered a savage laugh and attempted to sweep her into his arms. Gaby stiffened, sensing the innate brutality of the man. Brent's eyes narrowed and disappeared, but before he could make further overtures, a pair of brawny young arms like iron pinioned his. He wheeled, his jaw dropping. A grim young face with a tangle of blond curls above it was looking into his eyes squarely.

"Oxmoor!" blenched Carstairs involuntarily.

"The same," said the young man. "You thought you'd left me behind, didn't you? You forgot that I could follow you in my amphibian." And he felled Carstairs to the deck with a single blow like an Oxmoor had felled an invading Persian at the battle of Salami three thousand years before.

"Oh, Lloyd!" What a world of relief Gaby threw into that syllabus! He took her in his arms and crushed her to him.

"I got your telephone message just in time, lover," Lloyd said huskily. "Charlotte was at Hurley's early this afternoon and found Donald. He confessed everything."

"Then you found the . . ."

"Here they are, safe and sound," he said simply, drawing the garnets from his necktie. "The detectives didn't think of looking there."

Neither of them spoke, for somehow words seemed strangely banal against the tropic beauty of the lagoon. Captain Stannard, a white patch in the darkness, coughed discreetly.

"Steam's up, sir, awaiting your orders."

"Take the wheel and relieve him, Jack." Lloyd Oxmoor's voice was gentle and almost inaudible, for his lips were grazing on Gaby Birnbaum's hair. "Head her toward the South Seas, Stannard; I've found my pot at the end of the rainbow, old man."